# THE GOOSE THAT LAID THE GOLDEN EGG: Accutane, the truth that had to be told

By Doug Bremner

Published by

Laughing Cow Books

Published in Atlanta, GA, by Laughing Cow Books. 2014

3rd edition, original edition published June 28, 2011 by Nothing But Publishing Ltd.

Cover art by Bradley Wind.

This ebook is dedicated to my wife, Viola, and my children Sabina and Dylan.

Music lyrics are used with permission from Hal Leonard Inc.

## Books by Doug Bremner

*Does Stress Damage the Brain? Understanding Trauma-related Disorders From a Mind-Body Perspective*

*Brain Imaging Handbook*

*Before You Take That Pill: Why the Drug Industry May Be Bad For Your Health*

*The Goose That Laid the Golden Egg: Accutane – the truth that had to be told*

*The Fastest Growing Religion on Earth: How Genealogy Captured the Brains and Imaginations of Americans*

*A Fresh Look at Greed*

*You Can't Just Snap Out Of It: The Real Path to Recovery From Psychological Trauma*

*You can find links to purchase all books at:*

*http://dougbremner.com*

# Table of Contents

# CHAPTER 1

Palm trees lined the road leading from the Orlando airport. A few puffs of white clouds sat unmoving in the brilliant blue Florida sky. My seven-year-old son, Lucca, played a hand-held computer game in the back seat of the cab. My wife, Viola, and twelve-year-old daughter, Lucia, looked out the window. I rode up front, thinking about how much I would be paid for the lectures I would be giving over the next year or so. The year was 2001.

We checked into the Disney World Hotel and went up to our rooms. Lucca grabbed the room key and ran ahead. He opened the door, ran in and jumped on the bed.

"Is this our room?" he asked, excitedly.

"Get your bags, Lucca," I said.

When the family was settled, I headed for the courtesy room of the private company that organized medical education events on behalf of GlaxoSmithKline (GSK), the makers of the antidepressant drug, Paxil. They had invited me to give the kick-off lecture for their initiative to push Paxil into the market for people with anxiety disorders. They called it Psychnet. The plan was for me to give a lecture to a bunch of psychiatrists from across the country, educating them about the benefits of Paxil in the treatment of anxiety disorders, and they would in turn, for pay, fan out across the country giving lectures to other psychiatrists on the same topic. Not only would I get paid for doing this, but I would be tagged as a preferred speaker for their nationwide lecture series for psychiatrists. Over the next year or two, I would give about 15 talks across the country, with the usual price being $2,000 plus travel expenses. However, I learned that many of the speakers canceled at the last moment, so I could squeeze out as much as $5,000 for giving a talk at the last minute's notice.

I stood for a moment before the door and checked my suit to see if it had any spots on it. Then I knocked.

"Come on in, Dr. Bremner," an attractive and smiling Asian woman said as she opened the door. "We're going over your slides now."

The room was filled with a bunch of good-looking young people hunched over laptops who seemed bright and energetic. A floor-to-ceiling plain glass window looked out over palm trees evenly spaced over a closely cut green lawn with the blue of the Florida sea just beyond.

"How does this look?" The woman waved me over to one of the laptops.

I scrolled through the slides.

"You've got some great graphic art support," I responded. That brought on a spontaneous smile.

"Thanks, Doctor. Any corrections?"

"No, these look great. When do I go out?"

"Your talk is in 30 minutes."

There was a knock at the door. She walked over and opened it.

Scott Sproul entered the room. We had hung out together at a bar the year before and gossiped about the ups and downs of the pharmaceutical industry.

Scott was one of the most up-beat people I ever met. He was now head of the Paxil marketing team.

"Thanks for coming down, Doug." He slapped me on the back. "How's the family?"

"They're doing great." The attention made me feel uncomfortable.

"Have they ever been to Disney World before?"

"No, this is the first time. Thanks for the invite."

"Well, it's great to have you here, Doug. I think you're gonna really help us get our message out about Paxil."

"Glad to help." And I meant it.

"Here're some tickets for Disney World for you and your family, for the weekend."

"Wow, that's really nice of you. I really appreciate it."

"No problem. Ready for your lecture?"

"Yeah, OK."

We walked toward the lecture hall. He opened the door and slapped me on the back.

"Go on out there and sell some Paxil, Doug!"

* * *

A few weeks later I was coming back through the Hartsfield-Jackson International Airport in Atlanta after giving an out-of-town lecture, when I ran into Charlie Nemeroff, M.D., Chairman of the Department of Psychiatry at Emory University School of Medicine, in Atlanta, where I had just been recruited. He was an energetic and gregarious man who was in constant motion. Nemeroff was known as one of the leaders in the field of academic psychiatry, what we called a "shining light." A recent magazine article about him was called "Boss of Bosses," and prominently featured him on the cover, in a white jacket with his arms folded across his chest.

"How's it going, Doug?" he asked.

"Great. Thanks for the recommendation to be a speaker for the Psychnet program."

"We take care of our faculty at Emory. Hey, Doug. About that Accutane study you're doing?"

"Yeah?"

"Make sure you meet with the dean about it. He's a dermatologist. We don't want any political hot potatoes. And get the dermatologists involved. They can refer acne patients to you."

He looked tired. He'd probably been on the road for a while.

"OK, no problem."

"Well, I've got to run. Catching a plane to Fort Lauderdale to give a talk about norepinephrine and depression. Are you interested in norepinephrine, Doug?"

"Yeah, sure." Nemeroff had done some research on the effects of Paxil on the norepinephrine system. GSK was using that angle to market Paxil as being better than the other SSRI antidepressants. They were eager to get people like Nemeroff out there talking about the science behind it all.

"Ok, catch you later." He turned and walked off, pulling his rolling suitcase behind him.

I stood there and watched him walk away. While waiting for an appointment with him just after moving to Atlanta, I had seen his *curriculum vitae* sitting out on a table. It listed work as a consultant for the maker of Accutane, but it didn't look active, and he was consulting for a gazillion other drug companies, so I figured it was no big deal. Nevertheless, I felt a little uneasy. Whenever there was money involved, you had to be careful.

*Don't worry about it,* I thought. *Just meet with the people like he asked you to do, don't make any waves, do what you're told, and everything will work out fine.*

# CHAPTER 2

I started out my career at Yale University, in New Haven, Connecticut, in 1990. Every day for 10 years I drove to my job under slate gray skies with the heat cranked up in winter or the air conditioning on full blast in the boiling humidity of summer, parked my car on a street strewn with broken glass, and hurried through the ghetto neighborhood to my office. It was in an old Yale Nursing School dorm, condemned and waiting for the wrecking ball.

I became my "job," focused on the advancement of my career and getting approval from the higher ups at the university. I didn't have time for sentiment or emotion.

The assistant professors in the Yale Department of Psychiatry were a vicious group. We called it the "dog pack." You ran with the pack, and if you couldn't keep up, the hell with you. If the pack smelled your blood, they'd turn on you *en masse*. But you didn't think about it. You just put your nose to the grindstone and tried to get the funding to keep the whole business going.

That's why when this lawyer guy from New Jersey named David Affinito called me up about doing research on some acne drug called Accutane that I'd never heard of, I didn't try to get rid of him right away. That and the fact that, dreading confrontation, I could hardly say no to anyone.

Affinito read about my research in *Men's Health* magazine, showing changes in the brain when people get depressed. He asked if I could do some research to show that Accutane, the acne medication, affected the brain in a similar way. I said yes, we could, but I doubted that any organization would fund it, viewing it as too "high risk." If he set up a foundation and got private donations, he could donate the money to our program, and the research could be paid for that way.

After I hung up the phone, I thought some more about it. An acne drug that would make you depressed? Go figure. I didn't know a lot about it, but the whole thing sounded controversial. Stuff like that could derail your career. I'd had wing-nuts call me up plenty of times with their stupid ideas about research. Besides, I already had a lot on my plate. I doubted I would ever hear back from David Affinito, anyway.

## CHAPTER 3

On one day in 1999, while I was still at Yale and hadn't yet moved to Emory University, I was working at my desk when my research nurse walked in and handed me a card. "Someone's here to see you."

That would be the guy from Roche Pharmaceuticals, makers of Accutane. He called me the week before and asked to meet with me. Affinito found a guy from Ireland named Liam Grant who wanted to donate money for the research. His son killed himself while taking Accutane. After I told him to go start a foundation, I could hardly tell him to get lost, even if I wasn't that interested in the research. And our program needed funding. So I said OK to taking the money. I couldn't see any harm in meeting with the guy from Roche, so I agreed. Besides, we were always hitting up drug companies for financial support for our research studies; I always met with them when asked. We hadn't started the study yet, and any help we could get would be appreciated.

"John McLane."

"How can I help you?"

We shook hands.

"I understand you're doing a study of Accutane."

"Yes, I am. Would you like to help us out by giving us some Accutane for the study?"

"No, I don't think so."

"Why not?" I was surprised. The actual cost to pharmaceutical companies of making their own drugs was only pennies on the pill. So even if they weren't interested in the study you were doing, or, more accurately, didn't think it would advance their marketing plan, they still would give you free drugs.

"We don't think there's any association between Accutane and depression. So we think it's a waste of time and money to do research on the topic."

"But if there was an association, wouldn't you want to know it?"

"These papers show that there is no association." He handed me some articles.

I looked over the papers. The studies were paid for by Roche.

"Well, we're going ahead with the study anyway."

"Is this study supported by Liam Grant?"

"How do you know about him?"

"We're familiar with Mr. Grant. We're sorry for his loss. But it has nothing to do with Accutane."

"OK, well, thanks for your information."

After he left the room, one of my students came in.

"Who was that?" she asked.

"I don't know. Some guy from Roche. I don't know what he wanted. Didn't seem to be very interested in funding our study, though."

"Maybe he's afraid that we might find out something he doesn't like."

"Whatever."

# CHAPTER 4

*Chris Tremaine was a handsome 19-year-old from Lake Hapatcong, New Jersey, who lived with his mother, Ginny Palazzolo, and his stepfather, Jim Palazzolo. He had a close relationship with his stepfather. Chris was competing in weight-lifting competitions, where he wanted to look his best. His only drawback? Acne.*

*He went to a dermatologist, who gave him a prescription medication for the treatment of acne. In time he became withdrawn and started giving away his things. His mother thought that was strange. No one said that the medication could be behind it. No one said that there was anything to worry about.*

*Until one day when he was found dead by hanging.*

*His grieving parents asked a question already asked by several hundred other parents.*

*Why did this happen?*

\* \* \*

Shortly after giving my talk in Orlando, Florida, I was back in Atlanta. I walked into the building where my office was located from the parking lot out front. The old Georgia State Mental Hospital was bought by Emory from the State of Georgia for a pittance as a place to house its overflow of research faculty. Built in the 1950s, it looked like something from Stalinist Russia. The outside of the building was encased in a metal grid, which they claimed was put in place to reflect away the rays of the intense Georgia sun and save on air conditioning bills, but we thought it was put there to keep the mental patients from leaping to their deaths. They were long gone, however, and only their ghosts remained.

I hurried into my office. I had an appointment with an assistant professor of Dermatology, Dr. S. Dr. S. agreed to participate in the Accutane study, but didn't seem very enthusiastic. Impeccably dressed in her white coat, she got straight to the point.

"Why do you want to do a study of Accutane? It's a great drug."

"I have no quibble with Accutane. I just think that doctors and patients have the right to know the true side effects of any drug. Then they can make up their own minds about what to do."

"But it's a magic bullet for acne. Taking it off of the market would be a disaster."

"I'm a scientist. I do research on the risks and benefits of prescription medications. What is done with that information is up to the FDA. Not me."

The Food and Drug Administration (FDA) was charged by the US government to decide which prescription medications were safe for people to take. Another part of their job was to decide if a drug that was already on the market was not safe, based on new evidence that came in after it was approved. They called that surveillance.

I didn't feel like I was getting anywhere with Dr. S. After she left, my research coordinator, Samantha, walked into the room.

"What's up with her?"

"She's busting my chops about the Accutane study."

"She's been totally uncooperative. Our study is never going to get off the ground if we have to rely on her. And we haven't gotten any referrals from any of the other dermatologists we've contacted."

"Fine," I said. "Let's put out an ad and recruit the patients ourselves. I can treat them. At least with a psychiatrist following them, they won't kill themselves."

"I don't know how we're ever going to get this study done."

* * *

A few weeks later I got a call from a family in Tennessee. Congressman Bart Stupak told them I was doing a study of Accutane. They asked to meet with me. And so a week or so later, a middle-aged and sheepish-looking couple filed into my office with two teenage children. After they sat down, they told me their story.

"Our son here was prescribed Accutane for his acne," the father said. "It cleared up his acne real good, but after about two months, he changed. He got real withdrawn and stopped doing his homework. Didn't talk at the dinner table. Then things got real strange--"

"Said that Jimmy Hendrix was talking to him in the form of a monkey," the mother interrupted.

"Gave him a specific date when he should kill himself," the father said. The teenager looked on with a blank expression.

"So what did you do?" I asked.

"We checked him in to a psychiatric hospital the night before the date he was going to kill himself."

"Sounds like a wise move."

"Once we got him off the Accutane, he went back to his old self. Hardly seems worth it just for a few pimples."

After the family shuffled out of the office I mulled it over. I had just heard about a guy on Accutane who lit himself on fire and jumped off a bridge.

What was going on with these people?

* * *

Life went on and we slowly got our Accutane study off the ground. One summer day my wife and I put the bikes on the bike rack and drove the SUV to Stone Mountain Park, just outside of Atlanta. It was a brilliant bright Sunday afternoon. The Africa-like sun of Atlanta in summer made the colors of the plants and trees richer and deeper than the memories of plant life from my childhood. Our Cavalier King Charles Spaniel, Julius, sat in the back seat between the kids.

"Make sure you've got your helmet on, Lucca," I said as I started to wheel away from the car. The dog barked and ran alongside my bike. I was worried that his leash would get tangled up in the wheels of the bike.

We headed down a bike path that made a long loop around the large granite mass that was Stone Mountain. The sun glittered off the waters of the lake that partially encircled the mountain. Lucca zoomed by me and shouted over his shoulder. Viola and Lucia lagged behind.

"Let's stop over here," I called to the others. I got off and walked my bike onto a large grassy field. The view was excellent, the glittering of the lake with the cold slate gray of the granite behind. There was a light breeze. A few white clouds floated by in the sky. We opened the sandwiches we had brought with us. After lunch, Lucca and Lucia walked down to the edge of the lake with the dog. Viola and I lay on the grass and watched them play.

"We better get back home. I've got some stuff to review, and tomorrow is a school day."

"Are you going out of town tomorrow?"

"Yes, I've got a grant review committee in Washington, D.C."

"What time's your flight?"

"In the morning. Early."

\* \* \*

Later, Viola and I sat in the living room and chatted while we worked on our laptops.

"I was looking up the Web site of a guy who was friends with my mother," I said. "He owns a New Age bookstore. He said that your body emits a type of aura that can be measured."

"Doesn't sound very scientific." Viola didn't share my interest in fringe beliefs. She was a hard-nosed scientist.

"There's a type of aura called 'indigo' that is associated with people who are highly creative, but have trouble following the rules and regimented behaviors that our schools and public institutions impose on us. I think Lucca fits the prototype. The Web site also said that some indigo kids are actually beings from other planets who were planted here by their civilizations in order to learn more about humans."

"So you're saying Lucca is from outer space—"

"—remember how I used to call him a chip from outer space." I laughed.

"Mmm."

"They call them 'space kids'."

"So why doesn't anyone know about these people?"

"The government wants to keep it a secret—"

"—of course."

"You never know. Quantum mechanics says that our ideas of space and time don't hold water. A particle can be both a wave and an object at the same time. Heisenberg's Uncertainty Principle says that you can't measure both the position and the speed of an electron accurately. Just the act of looking changes the nature of a thing."

"What does that have to do with space kids?"

"They say that this life is just a way stop along the road of a greater journey—"

"—I'm not interested in religion—"

"—and that we carry our karma along from previous lives, and will all end up in some sort of repository of souls one day"

"—woo woo—"

"And that the space kids were sent here to infiltrate the human race and teach us how to love each other, not start wars, respect the earth, and move on through the path of the souls or whatever--"

"—oh."

"My point is that even physics tells us that we don't really know what is going on, ultimately. But we still think in terms of Newtonian physics. You let go of something, and it falls to the ground. They also say that the world will end in 2012. Do you know about the Mayan calendar?"

"No."

"They had a 260-day-long calendar year they called the Tzolk'in, which they combined with a 365-day-long calendar year they called the Haab'. The two combined formed a cycle of 52 Haabs they called the Calendar Round."

"So what?"

"They thought of time as cyclical. You know, birth-death. Renewal. That sort of thing."

"What does that have to do with Lucca?"

"I'm just saying that there are different ways of looking at things. It doesn't just have to be live your life, pay your taxes, die, pass your money on to your kids. That sort of thing."

"So Lucca was sent here to teach us something?"

"Who knows? Maybe we should ask him. Did you know that the Mayan calendar comes to an end in 2012? They say that will be the end of the world."

"I guess I'll have to hurry up and finish my research projects then."

"I think it would be great if there were space kids. At least I could be with my mother again."

"Ah, yes. Your mother."

* * *

Later I watched the television news, and they broadcast the strange case of Charles Bishop, who flew a plane into a building. Before he did it, he was heard saying that he was working with Osama Bin Laden. He was only 15 years old and was taking Accutane for his acne.

Roche provided an official statement. It was sorry for the Bishop family's loss, but Accutane had nothing to do with it.

While the press was sorting through the Bishop disaster, Congressman Bart Stupak, Democrat from Michigan, was standing on the floor of Congress, calling for a congressional investigation. His son, Bart Jr., was a 16-year-old boy who killed himself while on Accutane. Well liked. Captain of the football team.

*Maybe that Irish guy is on to something*, I thought.

# CHAPTER 5

Walking into the office the next day, I passed by Samantha's open door. She flashed me a quick look from her desk.

"One of the Accutane subject's moms just called. She said she stopped going to school and is crying a lot. She just had her post-treatment brain scan."

"If she is finished with her Accutane treatment, let's keep an eye on her. Have her come back in a week, and we'll see how she's doing."

"OK. The research fellows are asking for you."

I walked into the room where we kept the computers that we used for doing image analyses. A couple of the research fellows sat looking at a computer screen. Samantha followed me.

"These are the brain scans you were looking for."

"How'd it come out?" I asked.

"Take a look. This is a patient before and after treatment with Accutane."

I sat down and looked at the screen. The analysis of the data had been finished the week before. I was surprised to find out that Accutane did have an effect on brain function. We were now looking for a representative brain scan to visually show the results.

"Wow. It looks like it shut off function in the frontal lobes of the brain. That's amazing."

"Pretty good, huh?"

"I never thought this study would actually turn out to be positive." I looked at the others. "We'll have to send this in as a presentation at the Society for Neuroscience in San Diego. I better get going. I have a meeting with the dermatologists."

"You mean, Dr. S.?" Samantha said.

"One and the same. I'm trying to get them to cooperate on a study of the effects of Accutane on depression. Charlie Nemeroff said I should try to get them involved in what I am doing."

"Oh, OK, Good luck getting anywhere with her."

"He also said that if I was asked in court whether or not Accutane could cause depression, I should say that we need to do more research."

"Hmm."

I swung my Italian leather laptop bag over my shoulder and headed out the door for the meeting with the dermatologists. I thought some more about what Nemeroff had said. Saying we need to do more research was like throwing a foul ball on purpose. It implied that you needed more information before you could conclude that the drug could cause depression. That was the kind of thing someone from a drug company would say. It sounded benign, and was a fail-safe way for them to avoid responsibility for anything. More research is always a good thing, right? I shouldn't have been surprised that he said that, though, as he had a reputation for being a booster of the pharmaceutical industry, almost to the extreme.

The problem was that I didn't believe that we needed to do more research to conclude that Accutane could cause depression. I worried about what would happen in the future, when I would be forced to say something that went against what my chairman told me to do. I hated confrontations like that.

*Don't worry,* I thought. *It will take years before these cases come to trial. Besides, they will probably settle out of court, anyway. Don't worry about things that may never happen, anyway.*

\* \* \*

When I got to the meeting with the dermatologists, Dr. S. and the chairman of the department were sitting there waiting for me in their starched white coats. I felt uncomfortable. I started out.

"I'm trying to generate some interest in doing a study of the effects of Accutane on depression. We'll need to have multiple hospitals involved. That's why I wanted to meet with you and see if you could contact some of your colleagues at other universities to cooperate. I was planning on going to the FDA to see if I could get them to cooperate as well. It seems like it would be a win-win situation."

"This may hurt our ability to get money from Roche," Dr. S. said.

"Actually, we haven't been able to get money from them for 20 years," the chairman said.

"What do you mean?" I asked.

"We got into a patent dispute a while back," he said. "One of the Emory faculty was working with them to develop a new drug, and they said it was their intellectual property. We had to go to court with them. I think it is still unresolved. We haven't been able to work with them since. It's all tied up with the lawyers."

"So what's the big deal?" I asked, incredulous. "Why can't we do the study?"

Dr. S. eyed the chairman nervously. "We'll see what we can do," he said.

"OK. I'm going to call the FDA. Maybe they can twist some arms and get Roche to provide the medication for the study to cut costs."

\* \* \*

When I finally did get someone from the FDA on the phone, I was put on speaker with several other people on the other end of the line. I thought that was kind of weird. It was like they were trying to cover themselves or something, or they wanted witnesses to what they were talking about.

"We don't have funding to do research," said a voice on the other end of the line. "We count on the pharmaceutical companies to research the safety of their products."

"Is that realistic?" I asked.

"We think so."

I knew that the pharmaceutical industry had gotten legislation passed by Congress that required the FDA to budget more money every year for new drug approval, which meant that there was less and less to monitor drugs already on the market, since the overall budget remained fixed. The legislation also dictated that the drug companies pay the salaries of FDA employees, which was like putting the fox in the henhouse.

"That's not very reassuring," I said. "Couldn't you tell them that they have to supply the drug for the study?"

"We can't do that. We can't tell them what to do."

A few weeks before I had talked to one of the "foot soldiers" at the FDA who was working on Accutane. She told me that if there was a drug safety issue, all they could do was take the company to court, but they didn't have the budget for that.

When I got off the phone, I shook my head in disbelief. *Who was pulling the strings of these guys?*

\* \* \*

Next I called someone who headed up the dermatology branch at the NIH. He told me that he thought that the relationship between Accutane and depression was not "clinically relevant" to the field of dermatology. I couldn't understand. If the question of whether or not a drug used to treat acne was making teenagers kill themselves wasn't "clinically relevant," what the hell was?

I started to wonder if something wasn't seriously wrong here. Weren't these guys supposed to be public servants?

*Don't worry about it*, I thought. *Focus on getting the paper submitted for the upcoming conference in San Diego.*

# CHAPTER 6

*I think about death a lot. My mother died suddenly when I was four and a half years old. I think about her every day. She comes to me in my dreams.*

*I am a psychiatrist. And the son of a psychiatrist.*

*My father re-married three months after my mother died. When I was going around saying, "Where's Mommy, where's Mommy?" my siblings hushed me because our future stepmother was there.*

*Most people live their lives from beginning to end. Not me. I feel like I've lived my life backwards. So that the beginning of my life was the end. Like the sand crabs that dot the shoreline back at the house where we lived until my mother died. When you approached, they went backwards into their little holes.*

*The laws of physics tell us that a thing looks different depending on who's looking at it. Just the act of looking changes the nature of a thing. It's called quantum mechanics.*

*If you don't like physics, consider the fact that Denmark looks different, depending on whether you're in Denmark or gazing at Denmark across the Northern Sea from Norway.*

*I know other people have a different version of this story. And they say my version isn't correct. But you can't change the laws of physics.*

\* \* \*

The first case of depression after the 1982 American launch of Accutane arrived on the desks of Roche on May 20, 1983. By the end of the year, there were to be three more reports. On November 26, 1984, the first report of completed suicide came in.

By March of 1986, Roche had received six reports of positive rechallenge (people who got depressed on Accutane, got better when they went off it, and got depressed again when they went back on the drug). This was good evidence that Accutane was causing depression in some people. In addition, the babies of 40 mothers on Accutane died after being born with disfiguring birth defects. There were calls to take it off of the market. Although warnings about depression and other neurological side effects were added to the label, they were buried in the fine print along with dozens of other theoretical side effects, and were ignored by most dermatologists.

In 1992, a French dermatologist presented several cases of suicide associated with Accutane use at the 8th Congress of Dermatology in Deauville, France. His findings attracted the attention of the French Health Authority. They conducted a survey between 1992 and 1994, and found even more cases of suicide in people taking Accutane.

In the U.S., Roche was stating in private memos that there was a "problem" with Accutane and depression, although publicly they continued to deny that it was real. They said that depression was common in teenagers.

On March 3, 1997, the French product label was modified to include "suicide attempts" as associated with Accutane therapy, stating that "in rare occasions, neuropsychological problems have been recorded (behavioral difficulties, depression, convulsions and suicide attempts)."

The FDA didn't even learn about this until six months later. Naturally, it was chagrined, and asked the executives of Roche in the US what was going on. Roche said that Roche France was a different company than the Roche Company in Nutley, New Jersey. That is why they didn't know about the label change.

A review, however, of the corporate structure and relationships of the different Roche companies (which was only divulged after Roche was given a court order to produce it) showed that Roche France and Roche Nutley were both wholly owned subsidiaries of Roche Basel. Accutane was made in Switzerland and shipped to the US, where it was packaged by and sold by Roche Laboratories.

A year later, the label of Accutane was changed to warn about the risk of suicide.

But that was too late for Chris Tremaine.

# CHAPTER 7

The Buckhead Ritz Carlton Hotel in Atlanta was a symbol of luxury in a neighborhood whose name was a buzz word for luxury itself. If you turned your head sideways, however, you could see it as a high-rise prison. I drove out to the Ritz in my vintage 1992 BMW convertible to meet Paul Smith, an attorney representing families who had lost a child to suicide while taking Accutane.

A short man with a slow Texas drawl, Smith reminded me of a frog. He was famous for his involvement in a lawsuit against the Eli Lilly pharmaceutical company related to the case of Joseph T. Wesbecker. In 1989 Wesbecker had gone "postal," walking into his job in a printing store and opening fire with an AK-47. Wesbecker was on Prozac at the time, and Smith argued that the Prozac made him homicidal. Smith came to a "high-low" agreement with the lawyers representing Lilly, where they would get nothing if the jury didn't come to a decision, but would get a pay-out of several million dollars if they lost (and much more if they won). He was later accused of "throwing" the trial by making a lousy closing argument in order to get a certain pay-out. When I asked him about it, he said he had the flu that day. I wasn't sure whether I believed him. Anyway, the money he got from that trial allowed him to retire. But he got bored hanging around his house in Texas, so when the Accutane cases came along, he saw it as a challenge worthy of his lawyerly skills. Today he was flying in on a Learjet from Texas. He was keen to recruit me as an expert witness in the ongoing law suits related to Accutane and depression and suicide.

There hadn't been any research on the effects of Accutane on the brain up till that point, and since my study showed that Accutane affected brain function, I was instantly catapulted up to the status of world expert on the relationship between Accutane and depression.

There were a lot of Accutane cases lining up. It looked like I might make some money out of this, maybe even enough to pay off those expensive home renovations. Whenever the choice came up between the cheapo American light fixtures and the cool designer Italian ones, we always chose the latter. Now we were in over our heads in credit card debt to the tune of over a hundred big ones, and they had jacked up the rates to 28 percent after a couple of late payments. With two kids in private school to boot, we were having trouble digging ourselves out of a hole, and leap-frogging to the next teaser card wasn't working anymore. We needed to find a way out, and I was hoping that this gig would be the answer.

After parking my car, I walked into the lobby of the Ritz. Bellmen heralded my arrival by bobbing their heads like marionettes. Carved stone statues of English lap dogs lined the lobby. A group of women followed a tour guide. He lectured to them about the portrait paintings in the mahogany-lined walls of the lobby. They were the wives of the corporate types who stayed at the Ritz on business trips. The afternoon agenda likely included lunch and then shopping at the high end Phipps Plaza mall across the street. Gucci and Armani had stores there.

Waiting for the elevator in the lobby, there was a clean-cut guy standing next to me, talking on his cell phone.

"Yeah, Paul Smith flew down last night." *Was this guy working with us?* I thought. But it was weird. He didn't look like a lawyer. I decided not to say anything.

\* \* \*

"Dr. Bremner! How are you!" Smith drawled after opening the door of his hotel room to my knock. "Congratulations on finishing your study!" I told him previously about our results. We were waiting for the upcoming meeting in San Diego to make it public.

"Come on in! Do you want something to eat?"

"No, I'm fine," I said, settling into an armchair.

He sat down opposite me.

"Hey, there was a guy in the lobby talking about you. Is he working with us?"

His head jerked up.

"No. There aren't any more plaintiff lawyers coming to Atlanta today."

"Who was he then?"

He looked out the window. The glass-covered skyscrapers of Buckhead glittered in the brilliant Georgia sun.

"Who knows?" he said at last. "Roche plays dirty."

"You mean someone is following you? And me?" This was creepy.

"You never know. We do know that they hired private investigators to look into the backgrounds of the families of kids who killed themselves on Accutane. They would go onto a schoolyard and talk to their friends, find out if they smoked marijuana, that sort of thing."

"Do you think Roche knows we started up the study again at Emory?"

"Of course they do. They have a whole committee devoted to you."

"I'm not afraid of them," I responded. "Why would I be afraid of a drug company? I've published hundreds of articles. I know what I'm doing."

"You don't understand what you're up against. These guys are making billions of dollars off this drug. They see you as a threat. They'll stop at nothing to take you out. Do you think they will just stand by and let some psychiatrist from Atlanta put an end to their gravy train? Of course not. Not if they can stop you."

"But don't they have any respect for me as a physician and a professor?"

He grinned. "They present themselves as an organization that cares about people and their health. But they're no different from an organization that makes pencils or light bulbs or that sells gas for your car. They're a corporation, not a charity organization. Their only responsibility is to their shareholders. They're there to make money selling drugs.

"Roche hired a fancy Boston law firm to represent them. They've assigned a lawyer to the case named Colleen Hennessey. This is her only case, so you can bet she is going to be well prepared. You've got to know the contents of your report inside and out. Colleen is one cool cucumber. But don't let her rattle you. Remember, you're the expert, not her. If she asks you a question you don't understand, just tell her that we don't talk that fast down here in the South, could you please repeat it and go slower?" What we would call a shit-eating grin crossed his face.

"I'm not afraid of her."

I didn't give Smith much thought as I strolled out through the lobby of the Ritz. I spotted a nice pair of shades in the lobby gift shop. I stopped to check them out. Normally, I wouldn't give a second look to a pair of sunglasses that cost $400. But, I thought, who knows? With all that legal work I was going to be doing, what with 30 lawsuits in the courts and counting and me as the lead expert, maybe I'd make enough to be able to afford a pair of shades like that.
I piloted my car out of the parking lot of the Buckhead Ritz Carlton onto Georgia 400 South. I was feeling pretty good about myself.

* * *

That weekend, we went to Atlantic Station to go shopping for clothes. "Look, kids, this is the largest parking garage in the world," I said as I steered the family Jeep Cherokee SUV underneath the urban city-within-a-city with its cavernous multi-story underground parking garage. We took the escalator up to the light of day and headed for Dillon's department story. We breezed past the men's department.

Normally, I wouldn't go in, but now I thought I had a good excuse.

"I need a suit to go through these legal trials," I said to Viola. "Most of my suits have holes in them."

"We don't have a lot of money."

"But I'm going to be making a lot of money with these Accutane cases. That should more than cover it. And you don't want me to look bad in court, do you?" I knew that last one would get to her Italian sense of *bella figura*.

"OK, I guess so." We walked into the store and looked around. "How about this black one with pinstripes?" she said.

# CHAPTER 8

The Airport Hilton in Atlanta sat in the middle of a vast urban-suburban-whatever waste surrounding the Hartsfield-Jackson International Airport, like a crab that has been deposited far from water in the middle of an endless seashore. Connected with no community, it existed parallel to the other featureless chain hotels that littered the area. It waited to consume the lost waifs who entered into its clutches from the nearby airport, deposited *en masse* by courtesy buses.

They arrived not knowing or caring where they were, oblivious to the fact that escape on foot was impossible.

It was to this place that I drove one day in 2004. The venue was a meeting with Smith and Mike Ryan, an attorney who worked with Smith on the Accutane lawsuits. They rented a meeting room at the hotel. Ryan, dressed in ripped jeans and a sweatshirt, read a report, oblivious to his Blackberry that buzzed away on the table. I met him once before. That time he wore a pinstripe suit. My mind logged the contrast. Smith sat at the table like a contented Buddha, looking sideways at the few remaining French fries on his plate. When I walked into the room, his eyes rolled up into the top of his head.

"Dr. Bremner!" He rose to greet me.

Mike Ryan gave a quick glance up and went back to his reading.

"Your study is really having an impact!" Smith said. Our abstract for the presentation I was to make in San Diego just came online that week.

"Do you think Roche has heard about the results?"

"Of course they have."

"Do you think they were surprised?"

"They were shocked!" Ryan blurted out. "They never thought you would finish. They thought that if they could control the dermatologists, they could stop you from completing the study."

"What're you talking about?"

"Through discovery, we got access to the emails between Roche and Emory." Discovery was a legal term that referred to the court-issued subpoenas that were used by the other side of a lawsuit to get copies of all of your emails, documents, memos, or whatever that might be related to the case.

"We found out that they hired Dr. S. to keep tabs on you. Officially, she was being paid to give lectures on Accutane and the brain. You can bet she didn't say that Accutane could affect your brain function. They also emailed people at Emory for updates on how the study was going."

I couldn't believe it. "She never told me she was working for Roche."

"She sold you out, man," Ryan shouted. "They used her to follow your study progress from the beginning."

"No wonder she never cooperated or sent us any patients. I had to treat everyone myself. And I just met with her about getting a clinical trial started. I guess I wasted my time. I also called the head of dermatology at the NIH to get some cooperation, and he told me that he thought that it wasn't clinically relevant."

"Oh yeah, I know that guy," Smith said. "He was working for us, and then Roche got to him. They went to the head of Health and Human Services, which is over the NIH, and said that since the FDA is parallel to NIH and that they approved the drug, that he was undermining his own colleagues."

"That's ridiculous," I said.

"Well, it worked. They got him completely muzzled through their political contacts."

Ryan got up from the table. "We did a case one time where we got access to the training videos the drug company made for their drug reps. It was called 'Dodge ball,' and in the film the guy was 'dodging' actual balls, like the game everyone played in school. He'd say something like 'Gotta doctor that asks you about the risk of heart attack with our drug? Dodge it!' And then they would throw a ball at him, and he would dodge aside." Ryan jumped from one foot to the other to illustrate.

"That's incredible." These people never ceased to amaze me. "I guess they aren't lacking in creativity or imagination."

Smith leaned back in his chair, enjoying the show. "How about the one where they hired professional cheerleaders to be their drug sales people?"

"No wonder the doctors are trying to have sex with them all the time," I said.

Smith hunched over his document pile. Recess was over. "Do you want something to eat, Dr. Bremner? Come sit down now. We've got to focus on this case.

We've only got so much time, and we've got a lot to go over."

# CHAPTER 9

In 1987, Dr. Peter Schifferdecker, a Swiss scientist under the employ of Roche Pharmaceuticals, wrote a report for the US FDA saying that Accutane could cause depression in some individuals, and that patients on Accutane should be supervised for the possible development of depression. The marketing group for Roche in the US, concerned about the effects of this report, if it became public, on Sales of Accutane, as well as liability issues, got involved. They helped revise the report, saying that they had enhanced it. It was obvious what their real intentions were, however.

The death of Congressman Bart Stupak's son while taking Accutane led to congressional investigations that forced the FDA to convene their dermatology advisory board to discuss the issue of the relationship between suicide and Accutane in September of 2000. Roche brought along some of their experts, who stated that there was no relationship. Epidemiologists from the FDA discussed the fact that multiple cases of teenagers become depressed every time they went on Accutane was strong evidence for an association. They called for more research. Roche initiated plans to do studies, but a year later, these plans were mysteriously dropped, and the FDA suddenly decided that more research was not needed, after all.

Meanwhile, Roche convened a meeting of its own experts at the Ritz Hotel in Reston, Virginia. They

were a group of scientists and physicians who were
wined and dined for the weekend and paid a healthy
stipend for attendance. Most of them had a history of
consulting to Roche, having research projects funded by
them, or having gotten gifts for themselves and their
universities, paid dinners, travel and the like. Not
surprisingly, they concluded that there was no evidence
for an association between Accutane and depression
and suicide.

Not wanting to let the issue lie, Roche organized a
meeting of experts in Switzerland to review the science
of Accutane and related compounds that had biological
effects in the body. Roche paid stipends to the
attendees, who had the added benefit of getting to rub
elbows with other leaders in their fields. Roche paid the
*Journal of the American Academy of Dermatology* to
issue a special supplement related to the conference,
and then paid the attendees to write articles for the
journal. Not surprisingly, the articles stated that there
was no evidence for an association between Accutane
and depression and suicide. A member of the FDA later
wrote a letter decrying the shoddy scholarship of one of
the articles in the journal.

Dermatologists continued to prescribe Accutane
enthusiastically. Between visits for pregnancy tests
and labs, treatment with Accutane meant a guarantee
of eight paid visits. Doctors are businessmen, too, and
they did the math in their heads. The Roche marketing
machine fueled the expansion of Accutane prescribing.
Although it was approved only for cystic acne that
could lead to scarring, some leading academics wrote
articles that recommended Accutane use for individuals

who suffered "psychologically" from their pimples. Soon 80 percent of patients treated with Accutane had mild or moderate acne that would not have led to scarring. Roche continued to reassure dermatologists that there was no causal relationship between Accutane and suicide and depression.

Meanwhile, the number of known suicides in Accutane treated patients topped 300. The FDA said that the true number was probably ten times that.

# CHAPTER 10

I walked in the door of my house at the end of the day and went upstairs to put my bag away.

I didn't see my daughter right away.

"Lucia!" I called out as I climbed the stairs.

As I passed through the library on my way to the bedroom, something seemed out of place.

I stopped, turned. And then I saw it.

The window was wide open. And the screen was pushed out, hanging crazily from the window, about to fall to the ground below. I walked over to the window and looked out. *That was weird,* I thought, *why would someone want to exit a second-floor window?*

I walked into the bathroom. Some stuff had been taken out of some drawers. It was on the floor of the closet.

"Lucia!" I called, looking for my daughter. I found her in her room.

"What?" she responded.

"Were you trying on some of mom's clothes in our closet?"

"No."

"I mean, I don't care if you were."

"But I wasn't." She followed me back into the walk-in closet.

"I wonder how this stuff got onto the floor," I said. "Weird."

I called Viola on her cell phone and told her what happened.

"Maybe someone broke in," she said. "Is anything missing?"

I looked around. "Not that I can tell. That's weird. It looks like they found the jewelry drawer. But they didn't take anything. I wonder why not." I walked back into the library and looked at the window. "They must have been in the house when Lucia came home and then jumped out the window."

"That's a scary thought," she said.

This was giving me the creeps. "I wonder what they wanted."

\* \* \*

I didn't have much time to think about it. I had to catch a flight to San Diego for the 2004 Annual Meeting of the Society for Neuroscience. I drove to the airport, and eight hours later, I was sitting on the balcony of my hotel room in San Diego. I watched the palm trees in front of the hotel swaying in the breeze. The sun was setting over the Pacific Ocean. I mulled over the day's events. Who would want to break into my house? And steal nothing?

The next day, I headed for the poster session. Thousands of neuroscientists were milling around the vast convention center. I went to put up my poster with our study results. There was someone waiting for me. He stood there looking at my poster for 10 minutes.

"Do you have any questions?" I asked. He just shook his head and stood there, staring at the poster. He was making me uncomfortable.

Finally, after another 10 minutes, he left. Next I was approached by a young woman with mousy brown hair. "I'm a reporter. Do you have a moment to talk with me?"

"Sure, I think this session is over. Let me take my poster down, and we can go have a coffee."

* * *

I was back in Atlanta. Ryan and Smith flew in to go over the Accutane cases again. We were sitting in a conference room they rented at the Buckhead Ritz. Boxes littered the floor, and there were stacks of documents on the table. It was May of 2005. Our Accutane paper had just come out in the *American Journal of Psychiatry*.

"Congratulations on your paper coming out, Dr. Bremner," Smith said.

"Yeah, I was surprised, when I called the FDA, that they already heard about the results."

"Everybody has heard about the results. Congressman Stupak was standing on the floor of Congress holding one of your brain scans over his head."

"I got an email from someone working for Roche. He said he was a scientist and invited me to join their global brain imaging initiative. Do you think it was a coincidence?"

"Did you respond to him?"

"Not yet. I wanted to talk to you guys and see what you thought."

"When did he email you?"

"It was two weeks ago, one week before last Tuesday, I think."

"That's the day your paper came out," he said.

"Yeah, I guess it was…" This was weird. "What do you think they want. Are they trying to bribe me or something?"

"Well, whatever it is, it isn't good. Don't answer until we get more information."

\* \* \*

A few days later, I was sitting at a computer looking at some brain scans with one of the research fellows when a scruffy young man walked into the room.

"Are you Dr. Bremner?" he asked.

"Yes."

"This is for you." He handed me an envelope and turned and walked out of the room without saying anything else.

I opened it up. There was some legal language at the top about Hoffmann-LaRoche. Reading on, I figured out that it was a subpoena, demanding any and all materials related to the Accutane study, including brain scans, patient records, analyses, all copies of reviews from journals, any articles I read; it went on and on for pages. I felt panicked. The phone rang in my office across the hall. I walked out of the room and into my office to answer. It was Peter McCaffery, a scientist from the University of Massachusetts who performed studies in mice showing that Accutane inhibited growth of neurons in the brain.

"I just got this court order telling me to turn over all of the primary data from my study," he said.

"I know. I just got the same thing." Emails starting popping up on my computer screen. It looked like all of the authors on my Accutane paper had gotten subpoenas. I guessed that they weren't going to be too happy about working with me in the future.

"What should we do?"

I was freaking out. I didn't know what to do. "I don't know," I said. "I have to talk to Paul Smith."

# CHAPTER 11

The next day, I was sitting in the office of Kris West, the lawyer in charge of research compliance at Emory. You didn't spend time with Kris if things were going good. She was an intense woman with wire-rimmed glasses who jumped out of the frying pan of the corporate legal world into what she thought would be a peaceful university life, but what turned out to be the fire of academic politics and the policing of physicians and researchers. I spent quality time with her the year before when a couple of spiteful faculty from the psychiatry department at Yale made a bogus allegation of scientific fraud, and I had to go through an inquiry at Emory. They had found no evidence of fraud, and considered the case closed, but then a lawyer from Yale had a "hypothetical" conversation on a train with someone from the NIH's Office of Research Protection (ORP), who had gotten involved and was asking for more information.

"Between you and Dr. Nemeroff, the psychiatry department is a full-time job for me," she said. Nemeroff was undergoing an inquiry at the time for a failure to disclose payments from a drug company on one of his papers.

"Yeah, but I'm on the side of the good guys."

"Whatever. I got a 15-page subpoena from Roche Pharmaceuticals. They want any and all materials related to your Accutane study, including brain scans, patient records, analyses, all copies of reviews from journals, everything."

"I know; I got one too. Can they just come in and take everything, just like that?"

"Just like that. They got a court order. You have to comply with it." This was worse than I thought. I was terrified. There were thousands of questionnaires, brain scans, all kinds of stuff. *What did they want all that for?* I wondered. My mind ran through the possibilities.

"I want you to turn over the contents of the hard drive of your computer and of all of the computers of your staff," she continued. "Oh, and Dr. Adkison wants to meet with you tomorrow."

"That's great." Claudia Adkison, J.D., Ph.D., was the Associate Dean for the Emory School of Medicine, and its chief legal eagle. She asked to meet with you only when you got into trouble. As I walked out of West's office, I wondered what Adkison was going to say to me.

# CHAPTER 12

I parked my car in the Emory physicians' parking deck and slung my computer bag over my shoulder. Crossing Clifton Road, I made my way to the administration building. It was a 14-story glass-clad behemoth with no right angles. No metal grids over the windows here, I noted to myself.

I took the elevator to the fourth floor. Each time the elevator beeped at the arrival of a new floor, my anxiety grew. By the time I got to the waiting room outside Dr. Watkin's office, I was feeling freaked out.

Kris West was already there.

"Would you like some coffee?" asked the person who popped his head into the room.

"Yes, please."

"This Smith guy keeps calling me every 15 minutes," Kris said. "He's giving me a headache. I think I'm going to have to leave after this and go buy some magnesium at the health food store."

"I don't think they've done any controlled trials of that."

"I don't care. It helps me."

The secretary ushered us into Dr. Adkison's office.

Dean Adkison spent a lot of time worrying about appearances. To her, I was just another small fire to put out.

"What're you doing this research for, anyway?" She eyed me critically. "Are you just trying to make money as an expert witness?"

"No. I'm doing research to understand the potential risks of a medication that has been given to millions of people."
"What problem do you have with the pharmaceutical industry, anyway?"

"Somebody has to stand up to these people." I was getting fed up with this. "There have been hundreds of suicides reported. How would you feel if your kid took the drug and then killed himself? This drug was approved for severe acne that leads to scars, but because of the marketing done by Roche, they've pushed it on teenagers with just a few pimples. Eighty percent of patients treated don't even have severe acne."
"They've brought a law suit against us to get copies of all of the material related to your study. We have to hire an outside law firm to handle this. You're not helping Emory University. This is going to be a big expense."

"Aren't you supposed to be there to protect the faculty? Does that mean that anytime someone does a study and gets a result that a drug company doesn't like, that they can just come in and trample all over them, and the university will do nothing? What's the university here for, anyway?" I was throwing caution out the window. This was annoying.

"You've got to get approval from Emory University to be an expert witness. We're not going to approve this."
I walked outside and called Mike Ryan on my cell phone. "Emory said they're going to block me from testifying." An ambulance sped by, siren blaring.

"They can't do that. We've put a lot of time and effort into this. We've got 35 cases across the US. You've committed to being our witness."

"You didn't tell me there was a case against an Emory dermatologist." That fact had come out in the meeting with Adkison. "I can't testify against my own university." I felt as if I were going down the rabbit hole.

"I don't know about that one. I'll have to ask Smith."

"Something else happened that was weird. Someone broke into my house but didn't steal anything. Do you think Roche is behind that?"

"I wouldn't put it past them."

"Do you think it could be one of those private investigator guys they hired that you were telling me about?"

"Maybe."

"Nice guys."

"Oh, they are Lovelies, indeed."

## CHAPTER 13

After the meeting with Dean Adkison, Ryan and the boys threw some legal bullshit at Emory, and they gave me a temporary OK to go ahead with the Accutane litigation. And so a few days later, I was back at the Buckhead Ritz. Smith was waiting for me in the lobby.

"Now remember, don't let Colleen rattle you."

"No worries, no worries."

We walked into the deposition. There was a long wooden table in the center of the room. Colleen rose from the midst of her boxes of legal documents to shake my hand. She had a prim and precise look about her. This was going to be a long day.

Smith was at my left as I sat at the conference table and Colleen on my right. In between taking notes on a yellow legal pad, she outlined a square over and over until the pen tore the paper. I wondered how she handled toilet paper. Only a psychiatrist would think something like that.

The videographer hooked a microphone to my lapel and adjusted a camera that sat on a tripod nearby. The court reporter settled into her seat. "Going on the record at 9:07 a.m."

Colleen fired out of the gates. "Doctor, who is Liam Grant, and what is his relationship to you?"

"He is a man from Ireland who donated money for our research program."

"Isn't it true that he paid you money to do a research study that he could use in his law suit against Roche, from which you intend to profit?"

"He donated money for our research program. He didn't hire me to do a research study. I'm not working as an expert witness for him. He can't get more than $50,000 for his litigation, anyway. He's hardly doing it for the money. We can't do research with no money. Roche certainly wasn't interested in helping us."

"Did you ask anyone there for help?"

"As a matter of fact, I did."

Colleen shifted in her chair. "And what happened with that?"

"Someone from Roche came and wanted to talk with me about the study. I asked him if Roche would provide medication for the study. And he said no."

"Did he have the authority to approve your request?"

"I have no idea. But it wasn't like he said, 'Let me get back to you,' or anything."

Colleen was really digging into her yellow pad with her pen now. "OK, let's move on to something else. Did you get approval to serve as an expert today?"

"I'm not sure how to answer that question." My anxiety turned to dread.

"Are you familiar with your university's policies, Doctor?" she snapped, pushing a document across the table at me.

"Do I have to answer that question?" *This was being taken down as part of the legal record*, I thought.

"Answer the question." Colleen's voice rose a minute degree on the pitch scale.

"I'm not sure that I should." I looked toward Smith. The sweat was pouring out underneath my pinstripe suit.

"Answer the question!" Smith yelled. *Jesus. Wasn't he supposed to be on my side?*

"My understanding is, yes."

"Isn't it true that you in fact Violated your university policy by not getting pre-approval, Doctor?" She was really going at the pad now.

"Not to my understanding."

"OK, no further questions."

* * *

We walked out onto the sidewalk. I stood there for a while staring into the distance. Shoppers walked by with idiotic looks on their faces. They were on their way to Phipps Plaza across the street, eager to make their purchases.

"I don't want anything going into the record that can get me fired," I said to Smith.

"You have to answer the questions put forward to you by counsel."

"So what's with her? Is she trying to get me fired or what?"

"She'll do anything she can to block your testimony. She'll discredit you if she can, so that you're no longer a danger to them. Her job is to eliminate you. She doesn't care about you, or your reputation. They're making a billion dollars a year on this drug, and they won't let anyone get in their way. We got hold of one of their marketing presentations. They've got a slide that says, 'The Goose That Laid the Golden Egg.' It is one of *Aesop's Fables*. It's about Accutane, the golden goose that just keeps giving. They don't have to do anything about it. But you know how the real story ends? The owner of the goose gets impatient with having to wait every day for a golden egg, so he cuts the goose open. Then, of course, he doesn't have any more golden eggs. The moral of the story is, 'He who through his greed wants everything, ends up with nothing.'"

"Nice."

I drove back home through the oppressive Georgia evening, with the top of my convertible down. I was pouring sweat in spite of the air conditioning being on full blast. A line of mechanical engines of death stretched out along Lenox Road for as far as the eye could see. A billboard called out, "Jesus Is Coming Soon!" My brain crawled. I couldn't wait to get home and have a drink. So I could forget.

# CHAPTER 14

That night, my wife was out of town at a conference, and both of my kids were sleeping overnight at their friends' houses. So I was all alone. After that deposition by the Roche lawyers, I felt as if I had been hit by a truck and fallen into a toxic waste dump, in that order. It was five o'clock in the morning, and I was lying wide awake on my bed in my empty house, staring at the ceiling.

I didn't think a glass of scotch would do much for me, and I felt as if my heart were about to burst out of my chest. I decided to grab the dog and go for a run. I wasn't usually the jogging type, but I figured, what the hell? Maybe it would help my anxiety.

After running around the block, I felt worse. I started to feel nauseous for some reason. I stopped and leaned over into the bushes. I noticed a guy across the street, walking. There shouldn't be anyone around at this time of night. What the hell did he want?

I moved farther into the bushes and threw up. How humiliating. I dragged my sorry ass and the dog back home and fell on the bed like a zombie. After another hour, I finally fell asleep for a couple of hours.

* * *

The next day, my wife and kids came back home. I didn't say anything to them about what happened, of course. I wanted to protect them from the toxic sludge.

I didn't know if they would know what I was talking about. A lifetime of turning inward when under attack had become a habit for me. I did it again.

Later that weekend, I sat on the couch going through boxes of documents related to the Accutane cases.

My daughter worked at the computer nearby and listened to the song by Coldplay, "Don't Panic."

*Bones are sinking like stones*
*All that we fall for*
*Homes places we've grown*
*All of us are done for*

*And we live in a beautiful world (yeah we do yeah*
*we do)*
*We live in a beautiful world*

"I'm reading files from this drug company that makes an acne pill that made some teenagers depressed and kill themselves," I said.

"Why do they make a drug that makes kids want to kill themselves?" Lucia asked.

"They're trying to sell a drug that will treat acne. But it's got this side effect that it makes some kids depressed, and then they want to kill themselves."

"Isn't that bad?"

"Yes, but these drug companies are focused on making money. They want to promote their products, sometimes even at the expense of people's health. They replaced the drug safety committee with a bunch of marketing guys. So the point is to avoid bad publicity from drug side effects, no matter what."

These companies were creating a massive spin campaign. But the real agenda was making money. And if they had to sweep some bad outcomes under the rug to keep their billions coming in, they would do so. I'd been helping by giving paid lectures for them. They were using my reputation as a researcher to promote their drugs. They chose the slides I showed, so my lectures were really just disguised Sales talks.

I thought about the possibility that some kids had died, just trying to clear up a few pimples. I had a sickening feeling in my stomach.

# CHAPTER 15

When my mother died, I was left alone. I didn't know where this death place was, but I thought that if my Mom was there, maybe I wanted to go there, too. I missed her a lot, but when I tried to talk about it, I was told I was better off without her. That hurt even more, so I learned to keep my feelings to myself.

It was like there was a scab over my heart, and if anyone asked about her, the scab was reopened. I had two faces, one that was real and wounded, and that missed a woman scorned by my parents. I tried to keep that one hidden. The other was a false one that I showed to the world. It was trying to fit in, so I could survive. My stepmother used phrases like "get with the program" and "reality check." I quickly learned that the program and reality were hers, not my deceased mother's.

Every night, I kneeled beside my little bed and prayed to God. I asked Him to convey messages to my mother. I didn't know if I believed in God, but I thought that was my best chance to keep in touch.

I dreamt about my mother at night. One time, I had a dream where I was walking through a forest where everything was familiar to me, every leaf on every tree. I came upon a house with a little porch in a clearing. I opened the door, and there was my mother. Just standing there looking at me, not saying anything. When I woke up, I had this feeling that I dreamt that dream every night of my life. I also had the feeling that it was very real. I didn't know for sure if it was a dream or something that really happened to me. As if I had been transported somewhere else while my little body was asleep. Part of me was frightened, but another part felt consoled to see her again. No matter how much I tried not to think about her in later years, I always remembered her face from the dream.

Since I had no one to talk to about my mother, I visited her in my imagination, and then I said that imagination is real. And if imagination is real, I could be with my mother. After all, what is the difference between magical thinking and spirituality, anyway?

The Swiss psychiatrist, Carl Jung, described something called synchronicity, where two things happened in a different space and time, but were related in terms of their meaning, even when there was no physical connection between them. It was as if something happened that influenced the aura of another event somewhere else in the universe. When I read about Jung and synchronicity during my psychiatric residency training, I blew it off as crazy. But later I would have reason to pay closer attention.

In time, the dreams of my mother went away. I ended up denying my mother. I learned to call her by her first name, and to call my stepmother, "mother." I didn't have any pictures or mementos. None were given to me. I never had a trip to the cemetery. My mother became a ghost. Maybe I went along with it, for my own reasons. When you're numbed out, you don't have to feel painful emotions. And if those emotions cause conflicts with others, it can be easier that way.

* * *

In high school, I drifted, not knowing what I wanted. I was told by my high school algebra teacher that I would never get anywhere in life, which made me angry, so I resolved to do well in college. At least if I achieved academic success, people wouldn't have reasons to criticize me. From there I got into medical school, and then drifted into psychiatry.

I stumbled into doing research while a Chief Resident of Psychiatry at Yale, which extended into a junior faculty position. The Chairman of the department wanted me to do it, and I found I was good at it. I got pulled into the race to get more papers and grants, fighting it out in the dog pack for the approval of the pack leader, the head of the department. That led to the advisory boards for screening of mental illness, foundations that were little more than fronts for pharma. The pharma sponsored lectures. The dinners. The consulting boards. Chumming with the guys we called "The Shining Lights," the ones who got all the gigs, and who were picked up at the airport in limos. Who had their papers written for them and got paid for it anyway. The ones on the marquis at the annual psychiatry meetings. They were sometimes making hundreds of thousands of dollars per year in outside income from drug companies.

There was something wrong here. What if some teenagers really did kill themselves, just because they took a pill for pimples? And the drug company knew it but swept it under the rug?

Wouldn't that be terrible?

The injustice to me and to my mother was coalescing in my mind with the injustice related to the families affected by Accutane. The lies, the glossing over of reality, the distortion of truth. All in the service of making more money.

I got up to get a glass of water at the sink. Viola was making dinner.

"Remember how I wanted to find out who my mother's biological family was, because I felt like half of my family tree was missing?" I said. My family tree as known at the time is below.

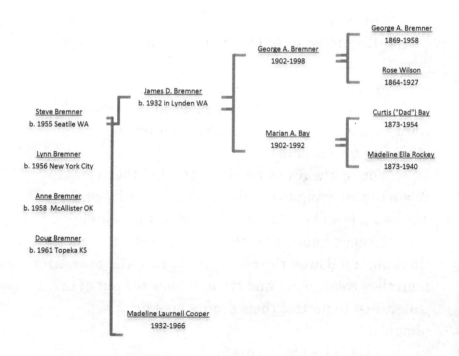

"Yes."

"I found out that my mother was born in Spokane, Washington, and that her mother was 18 years old and unwed. She lived with a birthing mother when she was pregnant—"

"-what's that?"

"It was a woman that the family paid to basically hide you until your baby was born and could be given up for adoption. It was to deal with the shame, I guess."

"You got her adoption records opened. Whatever happened with that?"

"I couldn't find the people on the birth certificate—"

"—why not?"

"--they must have falsified their names. I let it drop."

"Why?"

"I was worried that her biological family didn't want to hear from me. I was also worried about offending my parents."

"You're always worried about what they think. When're you going to cut the umbilical cord?" She dumped a box of pasta into a pot of boiling water.

"I know, know. This thing with Roche has got me thinking. I followed the rules, didn't rock the boat. And then they come along and try and blow me out of the water, just to protect their profits on a drug for pimples--"

"—you'd better be careful."

"If I'm going to get taken out anyway, why am I tip-toeing around all the time? Why don't I do something that is going to be good for me for a change, and stop worrying about what everyone else thinks?"

"I couldn't agree more."

And so began my quest to look for my mother's family.

## CHAPTER 16

But I still had Roche to deal with. I was back in the car, on my way up Georgia 400 to the Buckhead Ritz Carlton Hotel for another love fest meeting with Roche lawyer Colleen Hennessey. At the last deposition, she had handed me a 30-page report prepared by one of their hired guns and asked if I disagreed with any of it. Since I disagreed with pretty much everything, we spent the next three hours going through the report, line by line.

Colleen wore me down with her continual negative comments and shitty attitude. I felt like a seven-year-old with a negative, angry woman who commented on everything I said. And I wasn't any more able to get away from her than a seven-year-old. Paul Smith didn't make things any better with his continual outbursts and interjections during the depositions.

As I walked in, Colleen was standing there, chatting with a lawyer from Roche.

"How was Disney World?" the woman asked Colleen.

"Oh, it was great. My kids went on all the rides. It's one of the only places that both my husband and my kids like to go to."

I sat down at the conference table with the usual feeling of dread. The videographer hooked up a microphone to my lapel.

"Going on the record at 10:16 am."

Colleen put on her Roche face, as Smith called it, and turned to me. "Doctor, could you read the following note?"

She handed me a copy of a progress note from a patient's chart that had the patient's name blacked out. I read it out loud.

"The patient is a 17-year-old girl with acne who will start the Accutane study."

"Could you identify this document?"

"It looks like the protocol for our study on Accutane."

"Could you please turn to page 3 and read from the top of the page?"

I read out loud. "Subjects younger than the age of 18 will be excluded."

"Can you tell us why you would exclude subjects younger than age 18?" She was circling and stabbing her yellow legal pad with her pen.

"It is a Violation of the regulations to give radiation to individuals under the age of 18 without special permission."

"Did you get that permission in this case?" she snapped.

"Not that I know of," *Shit. Was this the end of my career?* Giving radiation to someone under 18 was a big no-no. That would probably trigger an inquiry.

"Dr. Bremner, haven't you identified the fact that you had a research subject who was 17 years old, that you in fact entered into a study, when it was clearly a Violation of your study protocol to include individuals under the age of 18?"

"I don't know. I'd have to go back over the records."

"I have no further questions." She gathered up her papers.

"Going off the record at 5:17 p.m.," said the videographer.

\* \* \*

As soon as I got back to the office, I went straight to Samantha's office.

"The Roche lawyers said that we studied someone under the age of 18. That's a Violation of the protocol to give subjects radiation under the age of 18. Did we do that?"

"Of course not—

"—you sure?"

"She was 17, but we waited until she was 18 to enter her into the study protocol."

I exhaled.

"These guys could have really cooked my goose. I was shitting bricks in there."

"They're just fishing—"

"--Why do you think they brought that up?"

"Looking for something to rattle you."

"They did a pretty good job of that. I can't believe how these guys manipulate the truth. They promote their drugs as working better than they really do, while covering up serious side effects of prescription medications, even deaths."

"Maybe you should write a book about that."

"Yeah, that's a good idea. But first I have to work on finding my mom's family."

"How's that going?"

"Her parents falsified their names on her birth certificate—"

"—that sucks."

"I'm having a hard time figuring out who they were."

"Wow. That could make things difficult. What do your parents think?"

"I haven't told them. I—"

"—you're gonna have to—"

"--I know. I don't think they'll like it."

"Yeah. Should be interesting."

# CHAPTER 17

That night, I retired to our mahogany-lined
library upstairs and pulled out a file with information
related to my mother. I hadn't looked at it in almost 20
years, since the last time I tried to find out about her. I
guess back then I didn't have the guts to push all the
way. One of the documents was a letter from the
Eastern Washington Adoption Society, dated 1933. The
letter acknowledged the application for adoption from
my mother's adoptive parents.

After several phone calls, I was able to determine
the current agency that had inherited the records of the
Eastern Washington Adoption Society. Since they were
three hours earlier on the West Coast, I figured they
would still be in. I felt nervous. I gave them a call. A
woman with a kind voice answered the phone.

"Hi, I'm looking for the adoption record of
someone named Lyndle Cooper who adopted a child
from your agency back in 1933?"

"Let me take a look." After a while, she came
back. "We haven't got a record of a Lyndle Cooper
adopting a child from our home. Are you looking for a
person related to you?"

"Yes, I'm looking for my mother. She died when I
was four and a half years old." I didn't see any point in
holding back the truth, even though it still hurt to talk
about. "She was adopted, and I had the adoption
records opened 20 years ago. I'm not sure if any of her

biological family is still alive, or if they even want to hear from me."

"I went through the same process myself." She had a comforting voice. "Nine times out of 10, both sides are happy that they connected with each other again."

"But I don't understand why there is no record of my mother coming from your home. She had to have come from somewhere."

"Not all children come from adoption agencies or children's homes. Back then, all you needed was a doctor's signature to take a child."

"Thanks for your help."

I went through my file again. I found some letters saying that my mother lived in the towns of Four Lakes, Washington, and later Reardan, Washington. Both were small towns in the middle of the vast wheat fields that cover eastern Washington. Her adoptive parents had both worked as school teachers.

I walked downstairs to talk to my wife.

"I'm not getting anywhere with this search for my mother thing. I think I need to do something more."

"Like what?"

"I think I need to hire someone to help me. This is really important to me."

"OK, OK, that's fine. Whatever you feel you need to do."

I went back up to the library and searched on the Internet. I found the name of someone from the Eastern Washington Genealogical Society (EWGS), a group that helped people do research on their family tree in the Spokane area. I emailed the contact person, and he responded, saying that he would do research for me for free, but they encouraged donations to the society.

A couple of weeks later, he wrote me a letter with some photocopied documents. They included entries from the Spokane telephone directory from 1933. Someone named Conlon had the same address as the person listed as Edward Conlon on my mother's birth certificate. Although there was no record of a birth of Edward Conlon, there was obviously a connection. Research into the census of 1930 showed that an Edward Ehrlich was living with a Thomas Conlon as a step-son. It didn't take a genius to figure that he had used his stepfather's name as a way to evade detection. The mother wasn't as easy.

Her name was obviously falsified on the birth certificate. I reasoned that if she falsified the name, maybe the age and first and middle names were correct, and she falsified only the last name. Going through the census records, I found a woman named Alice Rosenberg, who was the same age as the woman on the birth certificate, who emigrated from Vancouver, Canada, just before the birth of my mother, and was living with her parents in Seattle in 1930.

The birth certificate listed Alice as age 18 at the time of the birth of my mother, so that would be about right. But how did she end up in Spokane, where my mother was born, from Seattle?

I went back onto the Internet. I found several Alice Rosenbergs on whitepages.com who might be a match for my grandmother.

I decided to call the first one. Feeling like a nervous teenager calling a girl for his first date, I picked up the phone and dialed the number.

"Is Alice Rosenberg there?"

"Who's this?" barked the voice on the other end of the line.

"My name is Doug Bremner—"

"—what do you want?"

"--I'm doing some research on my family tree--"

"—I don't know you."

"—I know, if you'll let me explain—"

"I don't know who the hell you are! Don't call here again!" he hung up the phone.

I walked back into the kitchen where my wife was sitting at the counter.

"Boy, that guy was a real bastard," I said.

"Why, what happened?"

"I was looking for someone who might be my grandmother. And he told me off and hung up in my face."

"Maybe you should give up making these phone calls to complete strangers."

"Yeah, thanks for the advice."

I went back to our upstairs library and did some more searching on the Internet. I concluded, based on her age as listed on whitepages.com, that she probably wasn't the right match. From the census, I found the name of Alice's brother, and from his obituary, which I found online, got the names of his sons. One of them I found easily on whitepages.com. I also found on a message board that someone named Denise Ehrlich was searching for an Edward Ehrlich from Spokane, the name of my grandfather. With some more searching, I was able to find her phone number in Houston, Texas. I dialed the number.

"Hello? Is this Denise Ehrlich?"

"Yes, it is."

I introduced myself and explained what I was doing. "I saw on an online forum that you were researching Edward Ehrlich from Spokane. Are you related to him?"

"Yes, he was my grandfather. He came from Spokane, but he died 10 years ago in LA. That's where I grew up. My father's name is Thomas Ehrlich. I live in Houston now."

"Did he also use the name of Conlon?

"Yes, that was the name of his adoptive father. His real father was named Jacob Ehrlich. He abandoned the family when Edward and his brother were little. So are we related?"

"Well, I don't know if you want to hear about this. But--"

"--That's OK; go ahead."

"--An Edward Conlon was listed as the father of my mother on her birth certificate--"

"--What! That's amazing!"

"Yeah."

"--I never knew he had another daughter!"

"He did."

"Those people must be up in heaven jumping up and down saying, 'Rats! They found out about us!'"

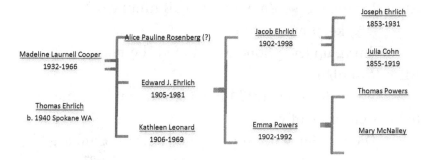

Now it looked like I knew about my mother's father's side of the family, which based on my research so far and what Denise would update me on looked like what's in the diagram.

But I still didn't know what her mother's side looked like for sure, the mysterious Alice Pauline Roserberg, if that was the one I was really looking for.

I laughed, "Ha, ha! Those guys didn't seem to be very good at keeping their pants on or their legs crossed. Did you know that Edward was Jewish?"

"Well, they always acted like devout Catholics, but I always suspected there was something more to the story."

"His grandfather is buried in a Jewish cemetery in Spokane."

"You're kidding! That's crazy!—"

"—It's true—

"--I don't think any of those people even know where Edward's grandfather is buried."

"Yeah."

"So what are you going to do next?" she asked.

"Well, I found the number of the nephew of this Alice Rosenberg, so I'm going to call him next."

"OK, keep me posted."

I hung up the phone and dialed the nephew of Alice Rosenberg.

"What do you want? I don't know you." He had a belligerent tone of voice.

"Did you have an aunt named Alice Rosenberg--"

"—What? Who the hell are you, anyway?"

"If this is a bad time for you--"

"—what are you asking questions about my family for?"

"I was trying to tell you—"

"--I don't know anything. I have PTSD from Vietnam, and I can't remember anything that happened before the war."

"Well, I'm looking for--"

"--My son is in the hospital," he shouted into the telephone, "And you're playing trivia games with me about some aunt, and I don't even know who she is. I want you to leave me alone!"

"All right, all right--"

"--If you want to know about our family, you can talk to my sister. I can give you her number. But don't contact me again. I mean it!"

I dialed the number of his sister next. I told her about my call to her brother.

"Oh, yes.—"

"I hope I didn't upset him too much."

"He's been having some trouble lately. I'll call him."

"And about your aunt—"

"—yes, I did have an aunt named Alice Rosenberg. She lived in Seattle."

"Is she still alive?"

"No, she died 10 years ago."

"Did she have any children?"

"She had one boy. He lives in Seattle."

"I think I saw him online, but his number is unlisted. Can I—"

"--He doesn't like to talk to people. Let me talk to him."

"Did you ever hear mention of a girl?"

"I think there may have been another child. Not with the man she married, but something before that. It was very hush-hush."

"What should I do?"

"I'm going to a dog show in Nevada next week. I'll see what I can do. I'll let you know."

She never called me back, but in the long run it didn't make any difference.

# CHAPTER 18

A few days later, I was back in the dining room of the Buckhead Ritz Carlton, having lunch with Smith and Ryan after four hours of deposition. I was drained, and I didn't feel I could do another four hours.

"I've been trying to get the NIH, FDA and other doctors to do a clinical trial of the effects of Accutane on depression," I said. "But I can't seem to get anyone to cooperate."

"You never know who's pulling the strings. Roche has got their fingers in a lot of pots," Smith said. "Just focus on what you're doing now." I wondered if that meant winning this case so they could get the big payoff. "You've got to know everything in your report like the back of your hand. You can bet that Colleen has it memorized."

"Yeah, I heard she's in love with her boxes," Ryan said.

"She takes them with her everywhere," Smith said.

"Does she take them to bed with her at night?" The waiter poured more coffee into my cup.

"Roche hired a psychiatrist from Harvard to go through all the suicide cases and come up with reasons why they weren't caused by Accutane. He calls them 'psychological autopsies.' He's a real piece of work."

"One of the only papers he ever wrote was a paper saying that Accutane didn't cause depression or suicide. Roche flew a bunch of their experts, including this guy, to a resort in Switzerland to have a conference about Accutane and depression. You can bet they didn't pick anyone that wouldn't endorse their opinion on the issue. After being wined and dined by Roche, they probably didn't feel like making a controversy. Then they bought an issue of the *Journal of the American Academy of Dermatology* and paid their experts to write articles based on the conference."

"Someone from the FDA wrote a very critical letter to the editor about the poor quality of the articles and their erroneous conclusions," Ryan said.

"I don't know how I got dragged into this mess," I said. "I always avoided controversy and confrontation like the plague. I've never been one to rock the boat. I just tried to keep my bosses and everyone else happy."

"Well, you're earning your spurs now, Doctor Bremner," Smith said.

"You've been getting better in your depositions over time," Ryan said.

"Yeah, well, practice makes perfect. But I don't think I can stand to go in front of Colleen Hennessey one more time. I've always been hypersensitive to criticism."

"Don't let her rattle you," Smith said. "Remember that you're the expert." My breakfast appeared in front of me.

"Look at this." Smith pointed at my plate. "Doctor Bremner, author of *Before You Take That Pill: Why the Drug Industry May Be Bad For Your Health*, is having a big fat cheeseburger for lunch. I thought you were supposed to be the all-natural health guru."

"Well, my daughter's a vegetarian, and rather than make two meals, we just eat vegetarian food for dinner, so I never get to eat meat. Besides, I need a load of proteins and fats to get through these fucking eight-hour depositions with Colleen, the bitch."

"Ha ha ha!" Smith said.

"These depos are really getting old. If I have to make another goddam trip to that hell hole Newark, I'm going to off myself."

Ryan worked over a piece of sausage with a knife and fork. "Colleen likes to get brownie points for how hard she works—"

"—Roche is paying her by the hour," Smith interrupted.

"--they wear you down, and then at 4:55 p.m. they spring a trick question on you, or some error they found in your data—"

"—-they're trying to demoralize you--"

"—they're doing a good job of that--"

Smith got up from the table. "It's five minutes to one. We've got to get into that depo. I don't want to give Colleen any excuse for asking for an extension of the eight hours she already has for today."

\* \* \*

"Going on the record at 1:12 p.m., afternoon of the seventh day of deposition of Dr. Doug Bremner," said the videographer.

Colleen Hennessey was sitting to my right, Smith and Ryan to the left. She had her pen and yellow legal pad at the ready.

"Doctor, could you take a look at what I have placed in front of you, marked exhibit 10, and identify it for me, please?"

"It looks like a copy of my report on Accutane and depression and suicide."

"Well, is it or is it not a copy of your report? If you wrote it, you should be able to recognize it, shouldn't you?"

"Yes, it is a copy of my report."

"Could you turn to the fifth page, third line down, and read what it says?"

"It says 'case reports of suicide and depression with Accutane.'"

"And did you in fact rely on case reports in coming to your conclusion that Accutane causes depression and suicide?"

"Yeah... I mean, that was one of the things."

"Isn't it true that case reports can't be used to determine if a drug can cause suicide and depression?"

"Along with other things, it can help inform an opinion about that. It is one of many things one can rely on to form an opinion."

"Doctor, can you identify this article for me, marked exhibit 11?"

"It is a case report of depression in a patient on Accutane."

"Could you turn to page six, and read the third paragraph?"

I read, "The patient was a 17-year-old boy who admitted to having used marijuana in the past."

"Is drug abuse associated with depression?"

"That depends."

"On what?"

"On how long it has been since the person used drugs."

"So is that one week, two weeks, one hour, how long?"

I can't say..." *Where was she going with this?*

"Why can't you answer the question, Doctor? Is that because you don't know?" Baffled again.

"No, I wouldn't say that."

"Isn't it true that this person became depressed because he was using drugs, and not because he was on Accutane?"

"Objection!" Smith shouted. "Ms. Hennessey, you are asking leading and provocative questions and putting words into the Doctor's mouth."

"I'm asking the doctor how recently drug use has to be to cause depression. Let him answer the question. Could you answer the question, Doctor?"

"Don't answer the question!" he shouted. "You're leading your witness, counselor. Are we here taking his deposition or yours? Counselor is asking leading questions. He doesn't know how and when this person smoked marijuana."

"Are you going to answer the question, Doctor, or not?" Colleen asked.

"Drug abuse could be a factor, but that doesn't mean Accutane didn't cause depression in this case. It looks like he hadn't used marijuana for several months, and then only occasionally."

"OK, let's move on," she said.

"Can I take a break?"

Walking out onto the sidewalk by myself, I stood there and stared into space. They only let me 10 minutes, and Smith sent me a text message asking me where I was, so I headed back in. After the break, Colleen had me read out loud about 200 reports in French that I had admitted in a previous deposition that I had read. I didn't see the point, unless it was just to wear me out. Then she pulled out a protocol I had written eight years earlier stating that the relationship between Accutane and depression was controversial. I responded that a lot of research had been done since then. And so we played the game of going through my report and identifying exactly which studies had been done since then. I was getting tired of her, to say the least.

Later, Smith told me that Roche claimed that some of the electronic files related to the imaging study had not been handed over to them as part of what is called the process of discovery.

It didn't matter that they were irrelevant to the study. Roche had convinced the judge that in doing so I was somehow concealing information.

That night, I felt as if I had run into a brick wall. I went back over some of the material related to the case, trying to make sense of it.

I couldn't wait until my Manhattan rolled over some of the rocky spots of my brain. After dinner, I had a couple of glasses of wine. Then another.

My wife went to bed early. I walked out onto the patio. The ground seemed to be turning. I crashed to the ground, whacking my eye on a flower pot.

"Get up, get up! What happened to you!" My wife pulled my arm.

"I fell," I said.

"You're totally out of it! I can't leave you alone out here! What are we going to do with you?" She dragged me into the house.

# CHAPTER 19

I made up excuses for the big shiner I had on my eye. I couldn't say, "I got screwed in court, got drunk and fell down." So I lied and said that I fell down the stairs by accident. It wasn't the first time someone told that lie.

That night, I trolled the Internet, looking for clues about my mother's family. Online, I felt as if I were inside of a protective cocoon, and none of the rest mattered. I was there with Edward, and Alice, re-experiencing their joys and passions, their hopes and fears, their utter failings. *Why had Edward's father abandoned him? Why did he deny that his father was Jewish? How had he and Alice met? Were they in love? Why didn't they marry?*

A couple of days later, I got a copy of Alice Rosenberg's birth certificate from the Canadian Office of Vital Records in Vancouver, British Columbia. I eagerly carried it upstairs to the library. It said that she was born in 1915, with the name Alice Gertrude Rosenberg. That was weird, though, because my mother's birth certificate listed her mother's name as Alice Pauline Woods. I could see falsifying the last name. But why the middle name? And another thing that didn't match was that the birth certificate said that Alice was born in Washington state, but this Alice was born in Canada. Why would you lie about what state you were born in?

That night at dinner out on the patio, my daughter, Lucia, was in rare form. She never let me get away with anything.

"Have you done anything to plan for our trip to New Haven?"

"I'm working on it."

"You haven't done anything. You're wrapped up in your own world," she said. "It's like we don't even exist."

"That's not true. I'm making arrangements to go to New Haven in August."

"I think we should stay with my cousins. I was chatting with Carla—"

"--Why should we stay there when their mother is in Italy then?" I interrupted. "We're going to stay with our friends."

"You interrupted me," she said. "You never want to hear what I have to say."

"No, I didn't."

"Yes, you did.

Viola scowled. "Why do you have to act like a teenager, anyway?"

"Oh, it's no use!" Lucia shouted, storming into the house.

Viola glared. "You're just like your stepmother. Always interrupting people—"

"--I can't believe you'd say that about me--"

"—you don't listen, and you tell people what they are going to do--"

"—I can't listen to this--"

"--It's true. You need to face the truth about yourself."

I grabbed my laptop. I was angry. Viola kept talking to my back as I headed upstairs to the library. She sent instant messages to my computer, but I ignored her. I trolled online through census records again. I thought more about Alice Rosenberg. I was uncomfortable about the idea of her as my grandmother. There were too many things that didn't add up, and talking to her family, I didn't get the feeling that I was related to them. I opened the file related to my mother's adoption again. There were letters from Judith Gilbert, the birthing mother, as well as the doctor, to the Coopers, who were the future adoptive parents.

There was also a copy of the baby book that my mother's adoptive parents made for her. There was a list of signatures of people who visited the baby. At the very top of the list was "Mr. and Mrs. Frank Gilbert." That was strange. I looked up some censuses and figured out that Frank and Judith were siblings, and that Frank was a neighbor of my mother's adoptive parents. It looked like there was no regular adoption, that the doctor just handed over my mother to her adoptive parents, just like the woman from the adoption agency said. The adoptive parents obviously already knew the family of the biological mother, or at least knew people that knew them.

Then it came to me. My sister, Lynn, wrote to me a couple of years ago. She told me that our mother's adoptive sister, Vinnie, told her that she knew who the family of our mother was. I'd never met Vinnie, and at the time I didn't believe it, and didn't think more about it. One more family myth, I figured. But now, I thought, if all of these people knew each other back then... With a growing sense of excitement, I rifled through the file. There was the letter. I eagerly scanned it.

Lynn wrote that Vinnie recounted a scene the year before where her own mother told her the name of our mother's half-sister.

Elinor Flood.

The name stared at me from the page.

A real connection to my mother. She was the same age as Vinnie. They were both one year younger than my mother, and both attended school in the small wheat-farming town of Reardan, Washington, where my mother's adoptive parents taught school, and my mother's biological mother taught as well.

I mulled over these facts for most of the following day. The idea that all this was a coincidence was hard to believe. Did my mother's adoptive mother know her biological mother? They must have. My mother and Elinor were even in the same class, since Elinor skipped a year. They were both being taught by a woman who was their biological mother. But neither one of the girls knew the truth.

That night, I was sitting on the couch watching TV with Viola when got Lucia walked in.

"You never leave room for me on the couch," she said. "No wonder I didn't want to move back here from my year abroad in Italy." My wife furtively moved to one side of the couch. Lucia sat down. I put my legs back up on the couch.

"I don't want you touching me," Lucia said. Viola got up and sat on the end of the couch.

"This is ridiculous," I said. "Why can't you let your mother sit on her own couch?"

"Don't tell me what to do! I hate you!" Lucia stormed out of the room.

"What's the matter with you?" Viola said.

"Why'd you jump up off the couch—"

"—I've got two teenagers in this house--"

"--I just snapped. But I can't stand seeing her tell you to get off of the couch—"

"—you're not acting like a parent."

"Why do you side with her against me?"

"You're not listening to me—"

"—we should act like two parents working together."

"But you don't act like a parent. You act like a child."

"Maybe I should just leave." I was fantasizing about jumping in the car and taking off. Maybe get a motorcycle to take off out of town.

"No, I don't think it would be a good idea for you to leave." I retreated to the library.

I sat alone and thought about my mother's half-sister, Elinor Flood. I looked up the census and found the name of her parents. Lloyd and Alice P. Flood. That was it! I had found my match! Next I found the death certificate for Lloyd Flood. I wrote away to the local genealogical society to ask them to get a copy of an obituary from the local library.

The next few days I anxiously waited for the obituary to arrive in the mail. When it came, I took it straight up to the library. It said that Lloyd Flood had been a wheat farmer his entire life. He had lived in

Reardan and spent his final years in Spokane. He was preceded in death by his wife Alice.

So my grandmother was dead. I didn't know how I should feel about that. One thing that was clear was that she had died before he did. So there never had been a time when I could have contacted her without him around. And I felt pretty sure he wouldn't have wanted to hear from me.

The obituary listed a surviving grand-daughter as Elinor Iverson of Spokane. There was Elinor Flood with her married name. I looked her up on whitepages.com. She was right there, plain as day.

I picked up the phone to ring her number. My hand was shaking slightly. I was scared, but excited as well.

"Hello?" came the voice at the other end of the line.

"Hello, my name is Doug Bremner. I'm doing some research on my family, and I wanted to ask you a few questions. Is that OK?"

There was a slight pause. "I guess so."

"Are you the daughter of Lloyd and Alice Flood?"

"Yes, I am."

"Are you aware that Alice had another daughter other than you?"

There was a pause at the other end of the line. "I am aware that that might be a possibility."

"What do you mean?"

"Well, the first time I ever got my birth certificate, I noticed that it said that there was another child born before me. When I asked my father about it, he got very angry and told me to never bring that up with my mother, to never talk about it again. He said that that would make my mother very upset, so I never brought it up again."

"That's interesting."

"You know, this is quite a lot of information for me. My mother would have been horrified to have this information come out—"

"—that's fine."

"Her generation didn't talk about these things."

"Can I call you again?"

"They were very hush-hush about this sort of thing."

"I've got to go to New Jersey tomorrow for some hearings related to lawsuits about an acne drug that can cause depression."

"I worked as a legal aid. Before my husband died."

"Can I call you from there?"

"I don't know. I guess it would be all right."

"I feel a special connection with you."

"Well, I have to go now."

"Goodbye." As I hung up the phone, I felt my heart rising in my chest. Was this the piece that had been missing from my life?

I now had filled out my mother's mother's side of the family.

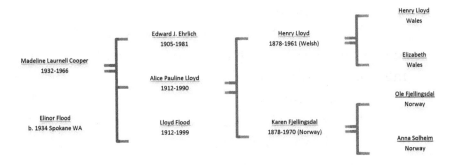

Madeline Laurnell Cooper
1932-1966

Elinor Flood
b. 1934 Spokane WA

Edward J. Ehrlich
1905-1981

Alice Pauline Lloyd
1912-1990

Lloyd Flood
1912-1999

Henry Lloyd
1878-1961 (Welsh)

Karen Fjellingsdal
1878-1970 (Norway)

Henry Lloyd
Wales

Elizabeth
Wales

Ole Fjellingsdal
Norway

Anna Solheim
Norway

# CHAPTER 20

ge ·ne ·al ·o ·gy(jn-l-j, -l-, jn-)

n. pl. ge ·ne ·al ·o ·gies

1. A record or table of the descent of a person, family, or group from an ancestor or ancestors; a family tree.

2. Direct descent from an ancestor; lineage or pedigree.

3. The study or investigation of ancestry and family histories.

\* \* \*

The derivation of the word *genealogy* literally means a written record (*logos*) of one's family (*geneo*).

The ancient Romans venerated their ancestors. They kept images of them that they worshiped. The practice was also common in China and other Asian countries. "Ancestor worship" is a belief that deceased family members have a continued existence, take an interest in the affairs of the world, and possess the ability to influence the fortune of the living. Some people believe that continued care for the dead is required for their well-being. Others think that devotion to dead ancestors is a matter of duty, regardless of what effects may come from that.

For some people, it can become an obsession.

# CHAPTER 21

The next day, I flew to Newark, armpit of the North Atlantic seaboard. Paul Smith and Mike Ryan were waiting for me at the airport.

Smith approached. "Hey, Doc!" he croaked. "How's it going, buddy?"

"Oh, just getting ready for another day of denigration and humiliation at the hands of Colleen Hennessey, chief counsel for Roche."

"Oh, come on, Doc. Don't go neurotic on us again. When she throws a winger at you, ya gotta just strike back and hit 'er right between the eyes!" Ryan pantomimed a right hook.

"Yeah, well, we'll see about that."

That night in the Newark Airport Marriott, I called Elinor Iverson. I talked more about my life and the legal case with Roche. She seemed interested. I felt calmer, talking to her. I gazed out the window. The bright white lights on the planes shuffled around in the distance.

The next morning, Smith and Ryan picked me up in a chauffeur-driven car. The driver, a sad-looking, aging black man, pulled the car away from the curb.

"Hey, Joey, my man," Smith said to the driver. "What's new in Newark these days?"

"Oh, not much, Mr. Smith. Just mayors going to jail, that sort of thing." We passed boarded-up and abandoned houses with chain-link fences around them.

"Joey's the best driver we have. Always gets us to the courthouse in record time. He knows how to take the back ways. Isn't that right, Joey?"

"Yes, sir."

On the radio the newscaster said that the state department ordered another two million doses of Roche's Tamiflu to prepare for a possible bird flu epidemic.

"Hey, good news!" Smith said, laughing. "Roche is going to make a bunch of money on Tamiflu! That means they'll have more money to pay us for our Accutane cases!"

"How's the Bishop case going?" I asked. That was the kid who flew a plane into the building in Tampa, saying he was working with Osama Bin Laden.

"Going well," Ryan said. "We're getting a ruling on Roche's motion to exclude you as an expert next week from the judge in Florida. Oh, by the way, we did discovery on that guy from Roche who came to visit you when you were starting up your study at Yale. Turns out he was John McLane, one of their higher up executives."

"Wow! I thought he was just a drug rep!"

"Well, I guess you were something special, honey."

"Love you too, sugar."

We drove on through the bombed-out remains of urban Newark. Music was playing on the radio.

*Hang man, hang man. Hold it a little while.*

I recognized it as Led Zeppelin. We parked outside the New Jersey State Court House.

*I think I see my friends coming, riding a many mile.*

Right in the heart of downtown Newark.

*I couldn't get no silver, couldn't get no gold.*

It was more like a third-world country than a major American city. We walked into the court house and took the elevator up to the third floor.

*You know we're too damn poor, to save you from the gallows pole.*

When we got off the elevator, David Laffinita was standing there talking to a middle-aged couple. He introduced me to Ginny and Jim Palazzolo, the parents of Chris Tremaine.

"I can't tell you how much this means to us, Doctor," Ginny said. "I know that Roche has put you through a lot."

"I'm sorry for your loss." I knew how it felt.

"At this point, the most important thing for us is that justice is served and that no other kids are damaged by this toxic drug. If we can save one additional life," Jim Palazzolo said, "then we have done something important."

"All rise," the security guard said. The judge entered the room and sat down.

"Doctor, you may come up," the judge said. I walked up and took a seat in the witness box. This was weird.

"Do you swear to tell the whole truth and nothing but the truth?" the court reporter asked.

"I do."

"Counsel for the plaintiffs, your witness," the judge said. Mike Ryan walked up to the witness box.

"Doctor, is it your opinion that Accutane can cause depression and suicide in some individuals?" Ryan asked.

"Yes."

"And on what do you base your opinion, Doctor."

"Hundreds of reported cases of suicide of people who were on Accutane, over 30 cases of people whose depression got better when they went off the drug and got worse when they went on it again." This was going well so far.

"Isn't that called 'challenge-dechallenge'?"

"Yes."

"And isn't that evidence by itself for an association between a drug like Accutane and a side effect like depression?"

"Yes, it is."

"And what other evidence is there that Accutane can cause depression in some individuals?"

"The fact that the depression starts after you start the drug, and that other compounds in the same class, like Vitamin A, have similar psychiatric side effects."

"And Accutane is similar to Vitamin A, in the same class, is it not?"

"Yes."

"Which can also cause depression and psychosis in high doses?"

"Yes."

"No further questions, your honor."

"Counsel for the defense," the judge said, "You may proceed." Colleen walked up to the witness box.

"Isn't it true, Doctor," she said, looking at the floor, "That epidemiological studies are more reliable than case reports?"

"Well, you look at all of the evidence when you evaluate the safety of a drug. Not just one particular thing."

"But isn't it true, Doctor, that you relied on unreliable case reports, when epidemiological studies showed nothing?"

"Well, I wouldn't say that..."

"Your honor," she snapped, "the witness is unresponsive."

The judge eyed me sideways. "Doctor, I am going to have to instruct you that you are to answer the question and nothing else. Please do not elaborate. The air conditioning is not working in this court room, and I do not want to stay here any longer than we have to today."

"I'm sorry, your honor."

"Counsel, you may proceed with your witness."

"Doctor, I present to you what we have marked as exhibit 43. Can you identify that for me, please?"

"It's a spreadsheet we use to calculate the brain metabolic rates for our study of the effects of Accutane on the brain."

"And exhibit 44..."

"Another spreadsheet..."

"And here is exhibit 43..."

"That represents numbers calculated from the first two."

"So you would take numbers from the first two spreadsheets and use them to calculate the numbers in the third one?"
"Yes."

"And that represents brain metabolic rate?"
"Yes."

"Which your study results are based on?"
"Yes."

"And some kind of formula is used to do that?"

"Yes."

"That the computer does for you?"

"Yes."

"And you wrote the formula?"

"Yes."

"Is this it?" She handed me a piece of paper.

I looked at it. "Yes." I felt a cold wave of dread move through my body. *Where is she going with this?* I thought.

"OK, Doctor. Here is a calculator."

*Oh no, this is really bad,* I thought.

"Could you take the first two spreadsheets and the calculator and the formula and go to the display board and do the calculations for brain metabolic rate?"

I looked at Ryan. He had an alarmed look on his face. He shot a glance over at Smith, who looked as if he didn't know what was going on. Sweat was pouring out under my pinstriped suit. I stepped out of the witness stand and walked toward the white board. I had to will my legs to move forward. Colleen read out the numbers, and I wrote them down. This was bad.

"And what is your answer, doctor?" Colleen asked, quietly.

"8.52."

"And what does the spreadsheet say?"

"9.14"

"Why aren't the numbers the same?"

## CHAPTER 22

"Why aren't the numbers the same, Doctor? Did you make an error?" Colleen had me against a wall now. I was sweating profusely.

"I don't know. I'd... I'd have to take a look at it again. There may have been an error in the formula."

"Is this the first time that you were aware of this, Doctor?" the judge asked, leaning over the bench.

"Yes, your honor." I was humiliated. I looked over at Smith and Ryan. Smith was looking at the wall to his left. Ryan was staring at his lap.

"So that means that your paper as published is incorrect?" Colleen fired at me.

"Well, I guess so..." I stammered. "I'm... I'm not sure. Like I said, I'd have to look at it again."

"So are you going to withdraw your paper now, Doctor?" Colleen was practically sneering at me.

"No, I'm going to go back and recheck the numbers."

"Why do you refuse to withdraw your paper, Doctor!" Colleen said, her voice rising.

"Objection!" Ryan shouted.

"Doctor, what is your explanation for this?" the judge asked.

"I don't know. I'll have to take another look at it, like I said."

"Your honor, I'd like to move for an adjournment," Ryan said.

"Granted. See you tomorrow at nine a.m. sharp."

"All rise."

* * *

The sun was setting on the edge of the parking lots that stretched as far as you could see around the Newark Airport Marriot, located across a stretch of asphalt opposite the airport about as long as a mortally wounded man could drag himself before giving up the ghost for good. I was circling the hotel, with the cold wind blowing off of the New Jersey Turnpike, which ran by a few ball tosses away, the lapel of my suit jacket folded up against the cold. Colleen had stripped me to my core, and there was nowhere else to go. I was humiliated and ashamed. I turned to go back into the Marriot to face Smith and Ryan. The woman at the reception smiled inanely in her black jacket and white shirt. Old people shuffled into the restaurant.

"What the hell happened in there!" Smith shouted.

"People make mistakes. I can't control everything. I thought--"

"--Where the hell was the quality control?" he interrupted me. "Aren't you in charge of your team?"

"I'm sorry. Maybe we should just throw in the towel."

"Don't freak out and go neurotic on us now, man," Ryan said, walking out from behind his hamburger and beer. "We've got to go back to the basics and see if we can salvage this thing."

"I can't believe this—"

"--I can go over the entire data set and recheck it. I can repeat the analysis."

"What are we going to do?"

"Don't give up now, man—"

"--I'll call you." I was eager to get out of there. I went over everything and found more mistakes. But after I re-analyzed everything, the overall results were still the same. We discussed the situation at breakfast the next morning. That and the fact that Roche had found out about my dispute with the Yale psychiatrists, and they were going up to take their depositions, to see if they could dig up any dirt on me.

"They'll probably lean on someone at the NIH Office of Research Compliance (ORC) to pull my NIH research grants, and then my career will be finished," I said. The ORC was still inappropriately involved in the Yale dispute. I was suspicious that Roche was to blame. This was increasing my paranoia. "What do they want, anyway?"

"They're looking for dirt," Smith said. "If they can ruin your career, they will. It will serve their purposes. You should have figured that out by now."

"About that data thing," Mike Ryan said. "Why don't we go back in there and just emphasize how important it is for you as a scientist to get the results--"

"—yeah, the good guy—"

"--and how much effort you have put into double-checking--"

"—it's true. You know, after everything, the results are the same." So why didn't I feel more enthusiastic?

*  *  *

This was all starting to feel like a game. I knew I
had to keep fighting, but I just couldn't stand it
anymore. And then, to make matters worse, Charlie
Nemeroff had an article written about him in the *Wall
Street Journal* about how he written a paper favorable
to a new device for the treatment of depression, but
didn't disclose the fact that he served as a paid member
of the scientific advisory board. The device was made
by a company called Cyberonics. I had gone deep-sea
fishing during a meeting in Hawaii with Nemeroff and
the Chief Executive Officer (CEO) of Cyberonics after I
was recruited to Emory. Now the faculty at Emory
were writing a letter of support to the paper, and I felt
like I didn't want to be the odd man out, although I
already felt like I was involved in more than enough
controversy.

The worse things got, the more I thought about
Ellie Iverson. About life on the vast plains of wheat
farms in Eastern Washington. About things that
happened 50 years ago.

I made plans to visit the newly discovered family
members.

# CHAPTER 23

In the early 1990s, Cyndi Howells, a housewife from Puyallup, Washington, and a member of the Tacoma-Pierce County (Washington) Genealogical Society, walked into the annual meeting of the Washington State Genealogical Society, which was being held in her home town. Dressed in a bathrobe and her bathroom slippers, she held up a disk in her right hand.

"I've got 20 files on here," she shouted to the assembled amateur genealogists. "Each file is the address of a place on the Internet where you can find genealogical information. I'm going to see how many more I can find."

At the next year's annual meeting of the Washington State Genealogical Society, she came back with 50 more.

And the next year she had even more.

In 1996, she had over 1,000. She called her list cyndislist and used oznet to post it at www.cyndislist.com.

Soon she was crashing oznet. She had to move to a different server.

Cyndislist grew with the Internet to become the *craigslist* of the genealogy world. At last count, she had 264,800 links to different sites in 180 categories on her site, with over a 1,000 new links added per month, and over 22 million visitors. With 15,000 visitors a day, answering her email and working on her Web site has become a full-time job. *Newsweek* wrote in February 24, 1997, "The biggest boon to the heritage hunt has been cyberspace. No one has been more influential there than Cyndi Howells, a Puyallup, Wash., housewife who became obsessed with genealogy after tracing her own family tree."

That was the key word. *Obsessed.* Why else would an apparently normal person spend hours trolling the Internet to look for online ship passenger lists and other trivia.

*Why, indeed?*

# CHAPTER 24

I wanted to visit the new family members I discovered on my mother's side of the family. Most of them lived in Spokane. I didn't want to create a conflict with my parents over the fact that I was in the region and didn't go to see them, so I planned it around a ski vacation with them in Redmond, Oregon. I didn't know how they would react to my going to visit my mother's family, and I thought that if they got to see our kids, that might at least partially appease them. I minimized the time we were away from Redmond, and created an impossible schedule, as usual. Six hours of driving, see one family, stay overnight, see the other, and drive back.

It was December, 2006. On the way to Spokane, I got a call on my cell from Smith.

"We need to get your updated report as soon as possible."

"I know, but the judge made me go back and do 2,000 screen captures of the way we drew regions on the brains. It's taking hours. You guys haven't paid me in months—"

"I know, I know, it's hard. I had to give up my Learjet."

"Seriously." I looked out over the treeless, snow-covered plains of Eastern Washington.

"We'll get a check for you in the next two weeks. I have to have a conference call with the other attorneys."

"OK, great."

"Oh, by the way, good news. The judge in multi district litigation in Florida rejected Roche's motion to have you excluded as an expert witness."

"That's great!"

"Yeah, they showed a series of videos of you looking tired and defeated, but there were so many different dates on the videotapes that it backfired because it looked like they were abusing you by deposing you so many times."

"That's good news. I'm glad for the Bishop family."

"Yes, they have been taking a lot of heat. They got written up in *The National Review*, who made them out to be crazy trailer trash trying to make money off of a multi-billion dollar drug company."

"That's terrible."

"Oh, we made the trip to Yale."

"Yeah? What'd they have to say."

"Only one of them was willing to cooperate. He was fairly mild. He didn't have any reason why he accused you of fraud. He just said you 'acted suspicious.'"

"That's great."

"Yeah. We subpoenaed all of his emails. He emailed the other one right before your conference call and said, 'Let's have fun with Doug tomorrow.'"

"Have fun with Doug? That's a riot." The issue was related to the data in a paper I co-authored with them. We had a conference call to discuss the issue, but apparently they had already decided to mess with me, for reasons that were unclear, unless it was just pure malice. "So is that it for the Yale thing?"

"I think so. They didn't find anything to use against you."

"Well, there is still that Office of Research Compliance thing. I'm sure they are pulling strings with them."

"I haven't heard anything on that front."

"OK, I've got to go. We're on our way to Spokane to see some family members." I was feeling apprehensive about our pending family reunion, in addition to all of my other worries.

"OK. Have a good time."

\* \* \*

On the way to Spokane, we decided to check out Four Lakes, one of the towns where my mother lived as a child. Snow covered the stubble of wheat fields. The white treeless ground undulating in slow waves stretched as far as you could see.

We reached Four Lakes: a cluster of trailers and what my wife called Topolino (little Mickey Mouse in Italian) houses clustered together in a knoll with a dirty gaggle of trees scattered about. The place didn't even merit a convenience store. Whatever school might have been there where my mother's adoptive parents once taught school was long gone.

\* \* \*

Two hours later, we were sitting in the living room of my mother's half-sister, Ellie Iverson, the

closest thing you could get to her who was still walking
the earth on two legs.

# CHAPTER 25

In 1823, an 18-year-old boy from Palmyra, New York, was visited by an angel, who told him of some magical gold plates. Armed with special glasses, he was able to translate them into a book that told about how the lost tribe of Israel was visited by Jesus in the Americas hundreds of years ago. In 1831, he started a church in Kirtland, Ohio.

He later said that church members could act as proxies for deceased persons, baptize them, and "seal" them into family clans that would be reunited in Heaven. His successor wrote about "the perfect mania" that possessed some of his followers as they started "to get up printed records of their ancestors."

Over the next 168 years, 113 million people were introduced, after death, to the church.

Members of his church, called the Church of Jesus Christ of Latter-Day Saints (LDS, commonly known as the Mormons), are worried that their ancestors who lived before the beginning of the church won't be able to join them in Heaven. But in order to get them into the church, they have to figure out who they are first.

That makes them some pretty damn good genealogists.

They've got a vault carved into the solid granite of a mountain 20 miles southeast of Salt Lake City where they store information about the births, marriages and deaths of over 2 billion people, the largest single database on the details of the human race in the world.

Buried 600 feet into the mountain, protected by two
nine-ton and one 14-ton doors built to withstand a
nuclear blast, the Granite Mountain Vault isn't going
anywhere soon. Five billion documents are stored on
1.5 million rolls of microfilm and 1 ½ million
microfiche. Twenty-five thousand volunteers are
currently working to scan and index all of these
documents as well as put them on the Internet so that
one day soon you can access all of this data while
sitting in your kitchen in your slippers with a notebook
computer on your lap.

Ancestry.com, a subscription-based service started
by members of the LDS church, has 900,000
subscribers, and is growing. Ancestry put millions of
documents online, including five billion names. They
have census records for all of the US from the past 200
years, birth, marriage and death records, and more. In
May, 2007, they dumped the military records of all of
the soldiers who fought in all the US wars, 90 million of
them, online.

Genealogy is now America's number one hobby.
Millions of documents are being put online so that
subscribers can sit in their homes rather than traipsing
across the country in search of obscure church and
governmental archives.

Since LDS is the fastest-growing church in the
world, you have to wonder if the Mormons are onto
something. That connecting with the nodes of your
family, those linked to you by sperm and eggs and
DNA, looping simultaneously backward and forward
through space and time, like the drooping lines
connecting the electricity towers that move through

mowed swaths of forest in the rural parts of America, will lead you to paradise?

*Who am I to say no?*

# CHAPTER 26

"Would you like something to drink?" Ellie asked. She was a polite, white-haired woman in her 70s.

"No, thanks." I was nervous. I didn't want to come across as an alkie or something. Maybe this wasn't such a good idea.

"I'm fine," my wife said. We were both perched at the edge of the sofa.

"Dusty, could you get me my usual?" Ellie said. "Dusty drives a school bus when he's not making my life miserable. My husband died 10 years ago. Did you have a good drive?"

"Yes, thank you."

"And what are you doing for Christmas?"

"We're skiing in Redmond, Oregon, with my parents and my sister. We left the kids with my parents and just came up here for two days."

"We don't usually do much for Christmas," Ellie said.

"It's been real cold this year," her son, Barry, said. "Froze the garage door shut—"

"--Did you fix it yet?" Ellie asked.

"Not yet."

"Why?--

"--too busy at work."

His wife, Kayse, looked on in silence. *This is awkward,* I thought.

"Barry's our culinary expert. He manages an IHOP restaurant. So are you ready to go?—"

"—-sure--"

"--We've got a reservation at a restaurant in downtown Spokane—"

"—great view of Spokane Falls," Barry interjected. The conversation continued at dinner. Meeting Ellie in person brought home to me the fact that she wasn't going to be a replacement for my mother. When you watch these kinds of scenes on shows like "The Locator," where there is a joyful reunion and people find the missing pieces of their lives, you expect more. Maybe I had unrealistic expectations of the meeting. Or was there something more?

The next morning, we went to see Connie Martin, niece of my mother's father, Edward Ehrlich, and her husband, Lanny.

# CHAPTER 27

The rental car slowly climbed up the snowy hill toward the home of the Martins on the outskirts of Spokane. I parked the car in the driveway, and we started to inch across the icy asphalt.

"Hi, I'm Lanny!" an elderly but vigorous man bellowed out, waddling across the driveway. "And this is Connie! How're you guys doing?"

"Oh, doing well. Thanks for agreeing to meet with us." I was starting to feel a little more relaxed.

"Sounds like you're on quite a journey! Come on in and tell us all about it! You had some cemeteries you wanted to visit?"

We sat and looked through photo albums. I got the feeling that I could be related to these people.

I was feeling eager to get going, though. I was trying to run that ridiculous schedule I had set up with the sole purpose of pleasing everyone but myself. We got into their SUV and headed for the cemetery. We had to get back to Redmond that night.

"So, where're we going?" Connie asked.

"First, I'd like to go to the gravesite of Joseph Ehrlich, grandfather of my biological grandfather, at Mt. Nebo cemetery."

"Oh, that's my great-grandfather as well. We must

have driven by that cemetery hundreds of times. I knew he was buried in there somewhere, but we never stopped to look."

We turned into the cemetery driveway.

"Look at the gate!" I said. The Star of David was in the center of the wrought-iron metal arch that topped the driveway. "I told you we were Jewish!" This was feeling really weird.

"Oh, my goodness!" Connie said. "Dad always said we wouldn't have done well if we lived in Germany when they were under the Nazis, but I never imagined something like this!" We got out and walked toward the cemetery, our feet crunching in the snow.

"Look, the headstones are all written in Hebrew on one side and English on the other!" We walked among the headstones, uniformly granite and lined up in rows.

"Which one is Joseph?" Connie asked.

I checked on my Blackberry. "Section A, row 1, plot 13."

"Here he is," Connie said. "Look, his wife, Julia, is buried right by his side!"

"Looks like she died in 1919," I said. "She must have died in the Great Influenza Pandemic. My grandfather, Edward's, first wife, Laura Schemmel, also died young. She was only 21 years old. Edward managed to conceive my mother just a year later. He had a son who was only a baby when Laura died. Do you know what ever happened to him?"

"His name was Edward Joseph Ehrlich, Jr.," Connie said. "They called him Joe. Edward remarried and basically abandoned him to the parents of his deceased wife. That was another reason, I think, why my father had a negative opinion of Edward. Joe was raised by his maternal grandparents. He was a wild child, and they had difficulty controlling him. He ran away from home when he was a teenager. I heard he later spent some time in prison."

"What for?"

"Armed robbery, I think it was."

"Where is he now?"

"I don't know. I don't know what ever happened to him."

"Stand over by the tombstone," Viola said. She snapped a photo.

"I wonder why their tombstones don't have writing in Hebrew," I said. "All of the other tombstones have writing on Hebrew on one side, and English on the other. They were obviously Jewish, otherwise why would they be buried here?"

"I don't know," Connie said.

"Maybe it was because they didn't know how to read Hebrew," I said.

"I can't believe I lived here my whole life and never came here before," Connie said. We stood there for a while in the snow-covered cemetery. No one else was there. We each had our own thoughts. After a while, we got back into the SUV and drove to the next cemetery. I rode up in front with Lanny. Viola and Connie were in the back seat.

# CHAPTER 28

Lanny glanced at me briefly. "I understand you're a psychiatrist."

"That's right." I was feeling more relaxed now.

"He's got only one patient," Viola said. "Himself."

I laughed.

"I'm a retired psychologist myself." He told me about a new method of psychotherapy, and asked if I had heard of it.

"No, I haven't."

"Well, I highly recommend learning about it. He has written several books. I went to one of his workshops last year."

"That sounds interesting."

"So, are you on some kind of quest or something?"

"I guess you could say that." He was onto me.

"Do you know what it's about?"

"I wish I did. If I find out, I'll be sure to tell you."

"Are you looking for something?"

"I think so. But every time I think I know what I am looking for, it changes. Does that make any sense?"

"Yeah, I think so."

* * *

We arrived at the next cemetery. "This is where my parents are buried," Connie said. "Harold and his wife; he was the brother of Edward, your grandfather." We got out and walked toward the site where Connie said the tombstone was.

"They're set in the ground," Connie said. "Right about here."

"Let's see if we can dig them out of the snow," I said. We dug for a while.

"I think this is hopeless," I said. "Did you know that my mother's mother is in this same cemetery? Her ashes are in a crypt. I think they are in the mausoleum, over there." On the other side of the cemetery there was a large building. We walked inside. The walls were covered with plaques with the names of the deceased, their births and deaths, and sometimes a few sentimental words. We scanned the numbers, looking for one that matched Alice, my grandmother.

"Maybe she's over here." I led the way outside. A wall of marble-faced crypts was exposed to the elements. The Spokane River Gorge erupted like flowers in front of us.

"Wow, they really have quite a view from here. Oh, here's Alice! 'Loving wife and mother,' it says here. Loving wife and mother, indeed! To some, but not to others. And look, her 'legitimate' husband is right next to her! But no trace of my mother!"

Viola clicked a picture. "Yes, your mother is nowhere to be found, indeed."
We drove back to the house. I had a lot of thoughts going through my head.

"This has been great," I said. "Thanks a lot for taking us around."

"We're having a get-together for our family tonight," Connie said. "Do you want to come?"

"Sorry. We allotted only two days to come up here. My parents were already getting pretty uptight about the fact that I wanted to find the biological relatives of my mother, so we wanted to keep it as short as possible."

"That's too bad. My kids would have loved to meet you."

"I know. But we've to get going now to get back by tonight. It was great meeting you, though." We got in our car and headed back to Redmond.

\* \* \*

On the way back, we drove through Reardan, a lonely place 50 miles west of Spokane. A single grain silo with the word REARDAN printed in large faded letters announced the presence of the town from far away. The wind whistled through the houses huddling together in the middle of the vast plain. There was no one there, and no trace of a school house. Even the ghosts of my mother and her mothers and half-sisters had abandoned the place long ago.

In the middle of town, I took a left onto the highway heading south to Redmond. A few hundred yards south of town, I stopped the car by the side of the road, and we got out and stretched and took a picture. It was all white with specks of yellow wheat stubble peaking out through the snow and slow rolling hills with grey slate sky beyond. After a while, we got back into the car and drove south.

I had a lot to think about, not the least of which was worry about how my parents were going to react to this.

# CHAPTER 29

As we drove back to Redmond, the open plains of eastern Washington gave way to the rocks and pine trees of the mountains of eastern Oregon.

It grew dark. The trees seemed to be grabbing us from the side of the road.

"I can't see," I said to Viola. The road had so many curves it was dizzying. Time dripped away.

At last we got back. Cocktail hour was already in full swing in my parents' rented condo.

"How're the kids?" I asked. Flames fueled by natural gas licked over artificial logs in the fireplace. Drinking glasses stood in rows behind glass cabinets in the kitchen. The ice cracked outside. My parents and the younger of my two sisters were sitting around the living room.

"They're fine," my stepmother said.

"We had a nice trip to Spokane."

"Why'd you go?" my stepmother asked.

"I'm biologically related to those people. Why wouldn't I want to meet them?"

"Your mother's right here," my father said. "She's your family. She's the one who raised you."

"He's stuck on the death of Laurnell," my stepmother said. "Get over it. Move on. I want to know when you're going to get over it."

"I am over it. Like I told you--"

"--No, you're not," she interrupted.

"I'm tired of hearing this," my father said. "Move on."

"I don't know if I have a good answer for you." This wasn't going well.

"This is your mother. Right here," my father repeated. "She's the one who raised you. You should show some appreciation."

"I do have appreciation. I--"

"--When he was a little boy, he never gave me real hugs. He was always tight, like this." My stepmother made a motion of a board-like person.

"But I—"

"--He never showed me that he loved me."

"I do love you. I just wanted to meet my relatives, and find out if my biological grandparents were still alive. But I do appreciate what you have done for me."

"No, you don't."

"I'd like to say—" my sister started.

My father interrupted her. "--Laurnell was no good for you. There are a lot of things you don't know about her."

"I think I've pretty much heard it all."

"Oh yeah? Like what?"

"That she was a bad housekeeper. That she didn't keep track of the bills. That she--"

"--That was only a part of it."

"If you mean that she supposedly had an affair, I know about that, too."

"She had more than one affair."

"She was a slut," my stepmother said, practically snarling.

"She took you kids with her," my father said. "She

went to Seattle for the weekend with Gar Heath. She took you along with her when you were a baby and put you by the side of the bed."

"I don't know what to say to that. It's late. We'd better go to bed. Tomorrow--"

"--Don't leave," my father interrupted. "We're not finished with you yet."

"I really have to go," I backed out the door with Viola. "We have to check on the kids."

As we walked back to our condo, I felt a turmoil of emotion, and my heart was racing. The dwarf pines huddled on the side of the road, watching.

"They were something else. I tried to respond to them without getting too emotional. And I don't think I drank too much and said something I shouldn't have, do you?"

"I thought you did fine," Viola said. "There's nothing you can do about it."

"We have to get back to Atlanta tomorrow. I don't have time to deal with this crap right now."

# CHAPTER 30

"Watch out for this 'Dateline' woman," said the Emory PR person assigned to sit in on my interview. "She really burned us with a story she did about animal research last year."

"Don't worry about it," I said. "I've got it under control." The year was 2007. I was getting ready to be filmed for a story about a dermatologist who was killed by his patient who was being treated with Accutane. They want to talk to me about the psychiatric effects of Accutane, and whether it could cause someone to commit murder. I knew it would be controversial, and could be a double-edged sword. They could go with the Roche viewpoint, and paint me as some kind of crock, or go the other way, and make me a hero. But I was excited about being on a major show that could generate significant publicity for my new book that was coming out in a couple of months. I knew that Emory was definitely worried about the PR consequences of the show. Up till now, the media had always been my friend, but we would see.

"OK, Doctor," the "Dateline" woman said. "We're going live in just a moment." A Paul light on the camera lit up, indicating that taping was live.

"Spell out your name for us, please, Doctor?"

"B-r-e-m-n-e-r."

"And your title is Professor of Psychiatry--"

"--Psychiatry and Radiology."

"Right. Doctor. Tell us about your research."

"We did a study that showed that the acne drug, Accutane, affects brain function."

"And why is that important?"

"Well, the fact that Accutane can affect brain function provides a way to understand how Accutane can cause depression, psychosis and aggression."

"And do you think that Accutane caused this boy to murder Dr. Cornbleet?"

"It might have affected his behavior, but he seemed to understand what he was doing when he committed the murder." I was feeling nervous. This "Dateline" woman looked like a piranha. We went back and forth with a few comments. I felt like she was trying to trap me, but that she wasn't getting what she was looking for.

After a while she said, "OK, great. That's a wrap. I'll be in touch next week."

I felt relieved that it was over and excited about the publicity related to getting on "Dateline." When I did get the call from her, it wasn't what I expected.

# CHAPTER 31

A couple of weeks later, I attended the 20-year reunion of my medical school. I wasn't planning on going, but an old friend called me and urged me to go, and I thought it might be good to get away for a while and talk about something else besides Accutane. In between reunion events, I drove out to the old house where I lived. I wondered about a girlfriend, named June, who lived with me in the house, and whom I hadn't heard from in over 20 years. Back in the hotel room, I looked her up online, and when I got back to Atlanta, I gave her a call.

"Oh, my god! Doug Bremner? I never thought in a million years that I would ever hear from you again!"

"It's nice to talk to you, too," I said. "What are you up to these days?"

"I've got two teenagers that are driving me insane. Otherwise, not much that is interesting."

"Let's stay in touch. Let me give you my email address."

"OK, that sounds great."

After that, I emailed her and told her about my life, about the nightmare I was living through with Roche. I told her that I had loved her when we were together, and that I was sorry that I had never told her that at the time. I felt that my emotions were blocked because of losing my mother at a young age, and everything I had been through in my childhood, and I was sorry that my behavior had hurt others in the past.

Maybe I could use this renewed contact to make up for things, and learn how to express my feelings more. She emailed me back and said that she forgave me. She was very supportive of me in my struggles with Roche.

After that, I emailed her multiple times a day. I would tell her about my day, update her on the Roche cases, what I was going through. She would tell me about hers. Picking up the kids. The community organization meetings. She seemed really interested in the things I was doing. The more I wrote to her, the more I felt drawn in.

My wife was completely absorbed in her work, and I felt like she had gotten tired of hearing about Roche and Accutane and all of my other troubles. So I would just chat through email with June. When she was depressed, I would send her "good thoughts" to cheer her up, and we would play "read my mind" games. The fact that she was far away made me feel like I was going back to the time of my childhood, when I would use magical thinking to connect with my mother, even after her death.

It started to get weird. I would dream about Scott. And I was mixing her up with my mother.

# CHAPTER 32

I was getting excited about the publication of my new book about prescription medication, *Before You Take That Pill: Why The Drug Industry May Be Bad For Your Health: Risks and Side Effects You Won't Find on the Labels of Commonly Prescribed Drugs, Vitamins, and Supplements.* I had spent months researching the primary articles on the safety and efficacy of medications for a wide range of medical conditions, and I had learned that the way doctors and patients alike viewed medications was seriously flawed. With half of Americans on a prescription medication, and 80 percent on some kind of pill, whether it be a med, vitamin or supplement, something was seriously flawed. It was due to come out in March 2008.

The research nurse working for my wife in the cardiology department heard about my book and asked me to give a lecture for their weekly research conference. They usually had a drug company bring food for the conference participants. Since I was a psychiatrist, she asked Ed Crumbley, local representative for Janssen Pharmaceuticals, to provide lunch.

I had known Ed for several years. Janssen's antipsychotic medication, Risperdal, was being heavily promoted as safer than the older group of antipsychotic drugs. It cost 10 times as much as the older drugs, but the patients usually didn't see the bill, so it didn't make any difference. They pushed the fact that it didn't cause extra-pyramidal side effects, or twitching motions, unlike the older drugs, but glossed over the fact that it could make you blow up like a balloon and cause diabetes. Crumbley was deeply in bed with the Emory Psychiatry Department, and often went on fishing trips and other outings with the leading research faculty. Dr. Nemeroff was lead author on an article about the use of Risperdal for depression, a controversial topic because of the side effects, but Janssen was pushing it anyway and using Nemeroff to give talks to other psychiatrists on the topic. Janssen supported a faculty position at Emory, paid for stipends for a couple of post-doctoral fellows, and were generous with funding for research and attending meetings, not to mention all the money that some faculty got for giving promotional talks to other doctors in support of Risperdal.

Ed wanted to have lunch with me before the meeting. We met at a restaurant in Decatur, the small satellite city of Atlanta that was closest to my house and Emory University. It was a pleasant day, and the sun flicked through the leaves of the maple trees that lined Ponce de Leon Avenue, the main street that ran through the city.

The reason he wanted to have lunch was obvious to me. After the usual chit-chat, he dug right in. "Hey, I see you're giving a lecture next week in the series that we sponsor, called, *Before You Take That Pill: Why The Drug Industry May Be Bad For Your Health*. And you have a book coming out with the same title?"

"Yes, I do."

"What's the matter with you?" He peered into my face. "What have you got against the pharmaceutical industry?"

*I'm not making any friends here,* I thought.

"Nothing, I just think people should be able to educate themselves about the risks and benefits of prescription medications. My book isn't against the pharmaceutical industry. It's just a fair and balanced view of the published evidence. Have you read it?"

"We've done a lot of things for you guys. I don't see what your problem is."

"Nothing. I mean, you haven't even read the book. Why don't you read it first before talking about it?"

We went round and round for a while. It was clear I wasn't going to go anywhere with him. What did I expect? This was someone who obviously saw his career in the pharmaceutical industry as a blessing. And he didn't think like a scientist. It was more like you do this for me, I do this for you. The unfortunate thing was that so many so-called "scientists" in the field of psychiatry operated on the same basis.

We shook hands and went our separate ways. My lecture would proceed as planned, with lunch provided by Janssen Pharmaceuticals, makers of Risperdal.

# CHAPTER 33

I was working on my laptop at a Starbucks in Atlanta when I got a call on my cell phone.

"I'm the person that interviewed you for the 'Dateline' story on Accutane," said the voice on the other end of the line. "I called a representative from Roche for a comment. They said your research was discredited and that the judge in the Palazzolo case had excluded you as an expert witness. Do you have any comment?"

I was stunned. "I don't know anything about that. I've not been excluded from any of the other cases."

"Do you think there is any merit to what the judge said?"

"I'd have to take a look at what she said. But my research speaks for itself. I stand by the results of our study. I don't think I have anything more to say."

After I got off the phone, I called Mike Ryan. "Did you hear about me getting excluded in the Palazzolo case?"

"Yes, but her logic was wrong," he said. "She shouldn't have excluded you because you corrected some mistakes in your study. That study was only a part of the information you used to form your opinion."

Someone sat down at the table next to mine and opened his laptop.

"This is really embarrassing. I'm going to write a rebuttal to what she said."

"I think that would be a good idea. So we have it, just in case."

"These people are incredible. They just keep spending hundreds of thousands of dollars on expert witnesses and hire a team of lawyers to beat everyone into submission. It hardly represents justice."

"Hey, I know what you mean. Welcome to the club. The plaintiff's attorneys are starting to get sick of this litigation. The case of the Stupak kid got thrown out because the judge said that there was adequate warning on the label of Accutane that it could cause depression when he killed himself in 1999."

"That's absurd. They were handing out sheets with talking points to the drug reps, telling them how to respond when dermatologists asked them about depression. They told them to basically stonewall and tell them that suicide was common in teenagers, but that there was no evidence that Accutane caused depression. In fact, they told them to tell the doctors that Accutane made teens feel better about themselves, and cured depression."

"I know. They even did an ad campaign saying that Accutane could be used for the treatment of depression. The FDA made them pull it."

"What a bunch of slime bags." I changed the topic. "What happened with the Bishop case, anyway?"

"Bad news on that one, too. The family decided to withdraw."

"What? After all this time and effort?" I couldn't believe that, after all I had been through, the case was over, just like that. I was crushed. "The judge upheld me as an expert in that case. They were ready to go to trial."

"They just couldn't take having their personal lives dragged through the media. They couldn't go on. I couldn't force them to do it. I'm just as disappointed as you are."

"Well, I've got to get going. I've got a Christmas party at the chairman of my department's house to go to."

There I would get a chance to read the tea leaves and see if my stock was crashing yet or not.

# CHAPTER 34

Charlie Nemeroff, MD, had a huge house perched on top of a hill overlooking a lake in the Buckhead neighborhood of Atlanta. His Christmas parties were famous; he had to hire a bus service to ferry people from the parking lot of a local church, so many people came. He was out of town most of the time, flying around consulting to drug companies, mostly, but the annual Christmas party was one time when he was always there. Attendance was mandatory for the faculty in the Psychiatry Department.

Walking into the party with my wife and kids, I pushed past the crowd at the door toward the food table. After filling up my plate, I turned to my left, and saw my boss, Dr. Nemeroff.

"Hey, Doug, thanks for coming," he said.

"Thanks for having us."

"What's this I hear about you writing a blog, with titles like 'Flu Shots Are for Idiots'?"

"I'm just trying to make people think a little bit. I have a book coming out next month on drug safety, and I'm trying to promote it."

"But 'Flu shots Are for Idiots?' What's the matter with you? The Dean's been asking me, 'Who is this guy?'" The tea leaves weren't looking so good now. "We like pharma, right, Doug?"

"Yes, we like pharma."

"I want you to stop writing your blog."

"OK, fine." I was nervous. Yesterday I learned that Emory would not issure a press release for my book, even though it was already written. Now it looked like the administration was talking about me, and that I might have gotten on the wrong side of Nemeroff. With the Accutane story going south, all I needed was for Nemeroff to withdraw support. My career could be history, not to mention my job. Would I have to give up everything I had worked so hard for? Go back to writing Prozac prescriptions? It was a depressing thought.

I went back to the bar for another beer.

* * *

Later that night, I was reading an email from June and my wife came into the room and looked over my shoulder.

# CHAPTER 35

"What're you doing?"

I tried to shift my shoulder over so that she could not see the computer screen. "Just checking my email."

"You're spending all of your time on the computer these days. Who are you writing to?"

"No one," I lied.

Viola peered over my shoulder again. I had told her before that I had contacted June, but as I got more drawn into the email relationship, I tried to cover my tracks. I didn't know what was going on, but I knew my wife wouldn't like it.

"Is it that the woman from med school? Why are you emailing her all the time? What're you writing about?"

"Nothing. She has a friend who's depressed—"

"--that's it?

"--and she was asking my psychiatric opinion."

"Give me a break."

"At least she has time to respond to me, which is more than you can say—"

"--I told you, I have a lot of deadlines."

"You're always in the living room, staring at your computer--"

"—and you're in here staring at yours. I thought you were working on a grant application. I guess I was wrong."

"You shouldn't complain if I'm talking to someone else if you don't have time to talk to me. I asked you to stop working on Sundays, and you refused."

Viola looked over my shoulder again. "How many emails do you get from her anyway?"

"A few."

"It looks like she wrote to you at least five times today."

"That's none of your business. I can have my own friends if I want to." Viola walked out of the room. After she left, I opened the most recent email.

"This is getting too involved," June wrote to me. "I think we should stop emailing each other for a while."

# CHAPTER 36

I couldn't believe it. I was screwing up my marriage, my family. My career seemed to be in the toilet. And now June didn't want me to contact her anymore. My life was useless. Everyone would be better off without me. I thought about being with my mother again. In that place they all talked about. Was it death? If it was good enough for my mother, it was good enough for me.

*And the hardest part was letting go, not taking part.*
*You really broke my heart, oh.*
*And I tried to sing, but I couldn't sing, not anything.*
*That was the hardest part, oh.*

That song kept circling around in my mind. I didn't what, or who, it was about, though.

\* \* \*

A few days later, I got another email from June. I opened it eagerly. It looked like she changed her mind. We started emailing each again. Things were bad at home. I felt that if my wife didn't see that something was dreadfully wrong, she mustn't really care about me. The Roche lawyers were ripping me to shreds. Writing to June took me away from all that. I felt as if I were in a protective bubble and all my worries about Accutane and Roche and the relentless criticism that pulled me back into my depressed, childhood frame of mine, went away.

Still, it wasn't enough. I was losing my grasp on the world. I didn't know what was happening to me.

I was at work, trying to concentrate on a paper I was working on. I looked at my email. There was an email from June. I opened it eagerly.

"The husband, here," the message read. "I read the emails you've been sending my wife. Please don't contact her again."

# CHAPTER 37

I was stunned. How was he able to read these? I was angry and humiliated. I felt regret and guilt for my ridiculous behavior. This was crazy.

I responded, "OK." I resolved not to contact her again.There was a knock on the door. A scruffy young man walked in. "Are you Dr. Bremner?"

"I am."

"This is for you." He handed me an envelope and walked out of the room.

I opened it up. It was a letter from the editor of the *American Journal of Psychiatry,* the journal where my Accutane paper had been published, outlining accusations of fraud against me from Roche. They were demanding that our paper on Accutane be withdrawn. The letter from the journal was addressed to the Dean of the Emory School of Medicine, and I was copied on it, as was Charlie Nemeroff, MD. It requested that the Dean investigate the accusations, and then listed 25 papers I had published in the journal. The journal's editor said that if there was any suggestion of wrongdoing, that they should investigate all 25 articles I had ever written in the journal. So my entire career was on trial now?

A feeling of intense fear filled my body. I couldn't take it anymore. I couldn't sit still. I got up and walked outside. I went out to my favorite place: a greenhouse attached to an old mansion from someone in the Coca-Cola family that was next door to the building where I had my office. They had donated it to Emory University, and it was now abandoned. Green ivy laced through the broken windows. Shards of glass and dust were on the tiled floor. I sat there on a metal folding chair. I smoked and tried to collect my thoughts.

After a while, I walked back into the office and called Mike Ryan. "I just got a letter saying that Roche accused me of fraud."

"That's typical of Roche. Even after they've won, they continue to persecute you."

"The journal wrote to the Dean of my university, asking them to do an investigation. So now I have to go through another inquiry. And they gave a list of all the articles I ever wrote in that journal, and said if they found anything, to investigate all the other ones as well."

"Wow!"

"I don't know why I have to go through this. Just because some drug company frivolously accuses me of fraud, to harass me because I said something negative about their drug, I have to go through an inquiry? Why don't I write a letter to them and accuse one of their people of fraud? Do you think they would investigate that?"

"The journal is worried about their advertising dollars from the drug companies. Those drug companies throw a lot of weight around."

I was terrified. It looked like Roche was going to succeed in their efforts to ruin my career. And what if June's husband was able to find out who my wife was and contact her?

# CHAPTER 38

Ponce de Leon Avenue, the main east-west corridor in Atlanta, makes a perpendicular slash across Peachtree Street downtown, before it slices through Druid Hills, one of the earliest planned neighborhoods in America, on its way east out of town.

Druid Hills, developed with the assistance of Atlanta's leading citizens, including the family of the founders of the Coca-Cola Corporation, back at the beginning of the last century, is frequently referred to as the neighborhood of "Driving Miss Daisy," because of the fact that the woman who inspired the movie lived there back in the 1930s, and the movie was filmed there. The neighborhood had a fierce historical society that was laughingly referred to as the "Hysterical Society" by those who had to go before it to get approval for changes in the appearance of their homes.

Ponce de Leon Avenue was named after the fateful Spanish explorer who originally travelled to Florida in the 16th century, looking for the Fountain of Youth. He never found it, but because of the proximity of Georgia to Florida, and for some other reasons having to do a local well, the road got associated with his name.

Ponce de Leon Avenue was dotted with parks on either side as it snaked its way through the Druid Hills neighborhood. The parks, designed by Frederick Law Olmsted, the same architect who designed Central Park in New York City, were listed as the Druid Hills

Parks and Parkways on the National Register of Historic Places on April 11, 1975. The Olmsted Linear Park Alliance (OLPA) was formed by some of the locals in 1997 to restore the parks— Oak Grove, Shadyside, Virgilee, Dellwood, Springdale, and Deepdene-- to their original state.

Deepdene Park, conceived by Olmsted as the "primordial wood" of the parks, natural forest with a stream trickling through the middle wedged up against an open field rimmed with trees called "The Vale," was directly across from my house. It was a great place to walk the dog at night. The forest of oak, hickory, and tuliptree, with an occasional yellow slash pine, was very different from the forests of Douglas fir, cedar, Western hemlock, alder, and quaking aspen of my youth in Washington state. I knew, because my grandfather had always been very careful about teaching me how to identify the trees in our native Washington state.

## CHAPTER 39

After worrying all day that June's husband would try to contact my wife, I did my usual routine of walking the dog before going to bed. Viola was at the door when I got back. The look on her face confirmed my worst fears.

"I got an email forwarded to me from some guy. I guess he is the husband of your old girl friend? He sent me what you've been writing to her. Are you crazy?" she said. "You told her you can't stop thinking about her? What's going on with you?"

"She's just a friend." I was freaking out.

"Did you have sex with her?"

"No. I haven't even seen her. The last time I saw her was 20 years ago when we were dating."

"I've had it with you. I want you out of the house. Now."

I left. What else was I supposed to do? I drove around aimlessly for a while. I felt terrible. I had thrown my marriage in the toilet. And for what? Some stupid virtual relationship? I was angry and confused. As I drove, I saw a tree off to the side of the road. Should I drive the car into the tree? It might make things easier. I had failed as a husband. I wouldn't get to see my kids anymore. What a waste. I was pathetic.

I didn't sleep at all that night. At 8:00 a.m. I drove to my office. My mind was starting to slip. Suddenly, an email from Viola popped up on my computer screen.

Viola wrote that I didn't seem to care about her anymore, and now she didn't care about me, either. She thought that we had had a strong bond, but now she knew otherwise. She wanted me to go home and get my things, and leave.

I called her in her office. "Please don't kick me out. I've been going through a lot. You don't understand, after I started emailing June, communicating with someone I never saw, it was like when I communicated with my mother after her death, through my dreams and prayers. It made me start having dreams of my mother, and it was like I was seeing her and talking to her again, like when I was little."

"This is crazy. If this really is a mental problem, then you should go see a psychiatrist. But if you email her or contact her again in any way, we're finished."

"OK, OK. I promise. Just give me a chance."

* * *

The next week, I found myself in the office of a psychiatrist, Dr. S.

"I'm here because my wife said I needed to go into therapy. I started emailing an old girl friend, and I got over-involved."

# CHAPTER 40

"I have to let you know that if you're here because your wife told you to come," Dr. S. said, "we have to address that as an issue in therapy."

"I think I need to be here for myself as well." I was so confused, I didn't know what I thought anymore. I felt if I didn't do something that I am might go crazy. But even though I was a psychiatrist, I wasn't excited about the idea of psychotherapy.

"Why, what's the matter?"
"I keep emailing this woman, and I have a hard time stopping, even though it's ruining my marriage."

"Why do you think that you email her?" I told her about my mother, about the loneliness I felt. How having someone to talk to online made me feel.

"You feel a yearning, like the yearning you felt for your mother."

"Yes. I've been harassed and deposed 16 times by this drug company, Roche. This woman who is an attorney for Roche who deposes me is extremely harsh and critical. Going through the depositions makes me feel like I did when I was a kid. And now I'm going through an inquiry for fraud. I know I didn't do anything fraudulent, but what if something turns up I didn't anticipate? It's very stressful having your career on the line. And this has been going on for a couple of years. My life is like shit."

"That sounds terrible."

"Sometimes I think that everyone would be better off without me, including my kids."

"Can you ever think of a time when things weren't like this?"

"I remember being in the boat out on the water when my mother was still alive. The feeling of rocking, being down in the hold, the waves knocking against the side of the boat. I was just a boy."

"Sounds nice."

I told her about how I felt after my mother died. "I hate it when people say things like, 'Good thing you were too young to remember her.'"

"Losing your mother is a tragedy. It's the worst thing that can happen to someone, other than losing a child. It makes people feel uncomfortable when they hear about it, so they say something that they think will make it seem better. But it just makes it worse. The best thing you can say is 'I'm sorry.' It's better to not try and compare yourself to the other person or tell them that you understand."

I paused. There was something I had decided beforehand that I wasn't going to tell her.

"What is it?" she said.

"I had decided not to email my old girlfriend anymore after I got caught by the husband and he told my wife. I went for a couple of weeks. But then she contacted me again."

"How did that make you feel?"

"I felt a rush of excitement. But also dread, a fear of getting caught again. I don't want to wreck my marriage. I wasn't planning on telling you about this."

"Why not?"

"I thought you would disapprove, and tell me to stop emailing her. She said that she wasn't going to tell her psychiatrist, because she was going to limit herself."

"Why would I tell you to stop? If you said you wanted to run off with her tomorrow, I would just try to talk with you about your feelings about that."

"I guess I assumed you would tell me to stop. My parents were both in mental health, and they used psychobabble to try to manipulate us. I guess I'm not very trusting of the whole therapy thing."

"Well, that's all the time we have for today, Doug. I'll see you next week at the same time."

I walked out of the office, feeling awkward.

# CHAPTER 41

I looked at my Blackberry. It was time for my appointment with Dr. S.. I'd been worried about getting there on time. I always worried about that. I didn't know why. The first time I'd been 15 minutes late because my mind blanked out or something, but after that I was always on time.

I sat in the waiting room. Good choice of name, I thought. Should I put down the magazine? Or pretend to be engrossed in it when she finally did come out, so that I wouldn't portray my anxiety about whether she would show up?

Time crawled. The beige wallpaper of the psychiatrist's waiting room stared at me. I checked again. It was two minutes after the hour. Did I get the time wrong? I checked my appointments in my Blackberry. It was in there. Seven minutes after the hour. Where was she?

Thirteen minutes after the hour. I could no longer distract myself with the Blackberry. Where was she? Was she dead? I had the flu the week before. Did I make her sick? Had she lost interest in me as a patient? I felt nauseous. Finally, the door opened.

"I'm sorry I was late," she said. "I'm running behind."

I walked by her to the couch. Wooden.

I sat in silence.

"How did that make you feel, waiting?"

"Angry, I guess. I'm always here on time. I don't know why you can't be."

"I'm sorry. I'm human, and therefore not perfect." This wasn't the first time. She was four minutes late two weeks ago. "But I think it would be helpful to talk about. What was going through your mind when you were waiting?"

I told about a time when I was 10 years old. I went to the first Little League practice of the year. I was really excited. There was one other boy there at the field. We waited, but no one showed up. I felt an incredible overpowering anxiety. How could this be? What went wrong? He convinced me to wait for two hours. Finally, disappointed, we went home. I later learned that we had the wrong field.

"I think the way I felt was like the anxiety I felt when my mother left... and I waited... and she never came back. I don't remember very well. But I think that is how I felt." I felt nauseous.

"Those are very powerful emotions."

I kept talking. But I was angry. Just asking me how I felt about it wasn't going to make it any better. I didn't see how this was therapy. It just made me feel worse. Every time I came to talk to her, I felt terrible afterward, even when she was on time. I was nauseous, and couldn't talk to anyone for hours afterward. And I had this feeling that she disapproved of me, like my stepmother did when I was a kid, or was going to tell on me, even though I had no real evidence that she thought like that. She did the psychiatrist thing of not telling me much about herself or what she thought, so how was I to know? I could relate to my "fellow patients" whose comments I read on online forums who talked about feeling like a crumb on the floor of their therapists' offices. Even though she was pleasant, I still felt like that.

I remembered a book I read in residency about psychotherapy. It stressed the importance of starting and ending on time. I made a mental note to myself that I should get a copy. Was I going to teach her how to do psychotherapy now, so she could cure me?

After the session, I walked out to the parking lot. A wave of nausea passed over me. I sat in my car with the door open. I leaned over and threw up on the pavement. Fortunately, there was a car next to me, so no one noticed. I had a taste of bile in my mouth. I closed the door and drove away.

I headed north on Peachtree Industrial Boulevard. The faceless suburbs of Atlanta stretched out before me in an endless wave that emanated from the lifeless center of the city. I kept driving and driving, past Waffle House, Burger King, repeat. My thoughts were running on and on. I was angry at Dr. S. for being late. I was scared my wife would leave me. I was confused about my feelings about my parents. This was a good place to be anonymous. Waffle House, Burger King, repeat.

* * *

I was trying to read that night, but I couldn't concentrate. The more I thought about it, the angrier I got about the fact that Dr. S. had been late for our appointment. I had been put down enough. As if the humiliation of having my mother die suddenly wasn't enough, I was pushed aside, and my feelings were discounted after that. I had suffered in silence and endured. But now I wasn't going to take it anymore.

I decided to write a letter to my psychiatrist. I would resign immediately from her care. I might suffer, but the resignation of a well-known psychiatrist from her care would send shock waves that would have lasting effects, leading to a more honest and responsible conduct of therapy in the future. My personal sacrifice would have positive ramifications for the general good.

I set out to write my letter. I decided that I would put it in her waiting room before our next appointment, and then leave. Right there on the couch in the waiting room. Imagine her hurt and disappointment when she found the note. That would surely teach her a lesson.

In the letter, I said that therapy appointments should begin and end on time. That was consistent with the "frame" of therapy as outlined by the famous psychoanalyst Robert Lange. That she shouldn't have her sister practicing therapy in the same office. And that her Facebook profile shouldn't be public.

I was ready to deliver my letter.

# CHAPTER 42

"Wake up, wake up!" the voice said.

"What is it?" I said, groggily.

"You were kissing and hugging me in your sleep. I asked you what my name was, and you said June."

I woke up like a thunderbolt hit me.

"Get out of my bed!" Viola yelled.

I didn't know how to respond. I was stunned. I got up and went to the guest room. This was not the first time I had spent the night there.

The next day, I cornered my wife on the couch. "June emailed me again last week. I told her I had to stop this for the sake of our marriage. But I think that the email got me thinking about her again. I promise that I won't communicate with her again, and if she contacts me, I'll let you know."

"I'm going to let her and her husband know that I am aware that she contacted you."

"That's fine. I want to make it up to you. I'll do anything to keep our marriage going." I was really scared then. If I could reveal my inner thoughts in my sleep, how could I be safe? At my core, I wanted to keep my marriage together. This thing with the old girlfriend was just craziness, and was destroying my life. I had to make fundamental changes, starting from the inside. Not just on the face of things.

"I promise. Don't give up hope on me." She moved off the couch and walked into the other room.

A failing marriage wasn't all that I had to worry about. I was scheduled to go before the Emory committee appointed to review Roche's charges of fraud.

# CHAPTER 43

I waited outside the hospital clinic conference room where the appointed committee was meeting to review the allegations of fraud. Familiar feelings of dread washed over my body. I fought off feelings of nausea. I should have been used to this by now, but I wasn't. I struggled to keep my thoughts in control and not panic. *Maybe I should just throw in the towel.*

Kris West poked her head out of the door. "Come on in." I entered the room and made a fallacious attempt at a grin. There were five professors seated around the table.

I sat down at the head of the table and put my bag on the floor next to me. I tried to smile, but it came out more as a grimace.

"The proceedings of this meeting are to be kept confidential," Kris said. "Roche has accused Dr. Bremner of fraud in his paper on Accutane, and at the request of the journal, we are conducting an inquiry. We're just focused on the accusation of fraud in the paper he published, so let's stick to that. After today's meeting, the committee should issue its report in three to four weeks."

"So why did you use the methods of analyzing the brain scans that you did?" one of the professors said.

"That's what's been published in the literature. It's what everybody does."

"The radiologist who reviewed the study said it was not what he would have done," he said.

"That's the expert hired by Roche. Of course, he's not going to say that he would have done it the same way."

"Roche has accused you of fraud," someone else said. "Do you understand why they think that you committed fraud?"

"There were some mistakes made in the study, but after they were corrected, the findings were unchanged. There are always mistakes made in studies like this. The important thing is whether or not the results are changed."

"So do you know why they accused you of fraud?"

"Probably because the negative publicity associated with my research study is interfering with the profits from their drug."

Another professor asked, "Do you have a problem with the pharmaceutical industry?"

"No, only when they put making profits above the health of people."

This went on for a while. Then Kris said, "OK, that's enough for now, Dr. Bremner. We'll be in touch with you in the next few weeks with the outcome of the results of the inquiry. Thanks for your time."

I walked outside of the air-conditioned clinic. The intense Georgia heat kicked me in the face. The sirens of the ambulances screamed. A magnolia tree menaced above the clinic driveway, its loud white flowers leering as they moved in the wind. A wave of nausea passed over me. I tried to push it away. I shouldered my Italian leather laptop bag and walked back to my car.

# CHAPTER 44

I sat in Dr. S.'s waiting room. The talking in my sleep incident totally side-tracked my intentions to deliver my letter, telling her that she was fired for being late. I figured that dropping out of therapy wasn't a good idea if I wanted to save my marriage.

I had to do something drastic, and fast. I was desperate. When I actually looked at what it would be like to live without Viola, the picture was grim. I had to change fundamentally. Emotionally. In my dreamlife.

* * *

"My wife is going to kick me out again," I said, when I got into the room. I told her about the incident of talking in my sleep. "I got another email from my old girlfriend last week. I think that is what triggered the whole thing. I thought I could deal with it. I knew I had to give her up to save my marriage. But I felt like renouncing would be like repeating what I did with my mother."

"Sounds confusing."

"I know. I guess I'm just messing things up, as usual."

"You did what you had to do to survive. You couldn't talk about your mother when you were a child. You said you didn't want to hurt her feelings. But have you thought about your wife's feelings?"

"Yes. And I want to do whatever I can to keep my marriage."

"It's going to take a while. You're going to have to regain her trust."

We spent the rest of the hour talking about the Emory fraud inquiry and my ongoing struggle with Roche.

"I'm sorry, Doug," she said, "but that's all the time we have for today. We'll pick this up next week."

# CHAPTER 45

The music intercom system in the waiting room of Dr. S.'s office played Pachelbel's *Canon*. I remembered it as the soundtrack from the movie *Ordinary People*. It was the only movie my family ever connected to together. Or at least, my sister and I connected to it, which was better than nothing. The part that we related to was how a death in the family tore the family apart, through their grief. The boy had fallen off a sailboat during a storm, and his brother, who was with him, felt guilty about surviving. Ultimately the parents split up. Until then, I felt grief about the destruction of our family, but I didn't feel grief about my mother, at least on a regular basis, or more important, myself.

"I learned early on to keep my emotions hidden," I said in response to one of her questions once I got inside the office. "But at what cost to my soul, and my emotions? When I got married, I made a promise to myself that I would not mess up my kids' childhoods the way my childhood was messed up."

"Tell me about that," Dr. S. said. I told her about how I was hushed as a child after my mother died and my future stepmother was in the house.

"Like the drug company and your university were trying to shush you up. Sometimes people don't want to hear the truth if it doesn't fit in with their own self-interests."

"My father married only three months later, and we moved away right after that and lost all contact with my mother's family and our old friends. My father and stepmother told me I was better off without my mother, and that she was a bad woman."

"But your mother is a half of who you are. By putting her down, they are putting you down."

"I always tried to do what they said, always tried to be the good boy. Like one time I moved my step mother's purse off a chair to make room for my cousin to sit down at breakfast, and my hand was greasy and left a mark on the purse. My stepmother went ballistic and screamed at me and said I was going to have to pay for it. I think I must have done work in the yard for 20 hours or something to 'pay off my debt.' I stopped talking about my mother and didn't fight back when they put her down. It was like I internalized all that negativity. I feel guilty now about not standing up for her."

"You were a little boy. You did what you needed to do in order to survive."

"After she died, I started wetting the bed. And then one time, after we moved to the new house, our stepmother told us we had to go outside for the day. It was a Saturday, and she wanted to clean the house. We went outside and sat on the swings for a couple of hours. I had to go to the bathroom. But I was afraid to ask to go back into the house. So I just urinated in my pants."

"What happened then?"

"We just hung around outside. Then at the end of the day, we went back inside. I tried to pretend like nothing happened. But somebody noticed. My stepmother brought me into the laundry room and made me strip."

"What was that like?"

"Humiliating. My underwear and pants were all wet and stuck together. I don't remember what happened clearly, but I think she was annoyed, maybe even angry. I think I wet my pants multiple times, but I don't really remember."

"You were traumatized by your mother's death."

"When I was eight or nine, I still had a urine stain on the coverlet that went over my mattress. I was ashamed. It's weird, but I have never talked about this until now."

"Those are some powerful emotions."

"Even after I grew up and went to college, I didn't do anything in support of my mother. I just numbed out my feelings and never talked about her or thought about her anymore."

"Most people work on their childhood issues in their 20s. Losing a parent at any age is extremely painful, but for you at the age of five, it was even more deep and intense. And you were not given the opportunity to grieve. It wasn't until now that you were ready to work on it."

I told her about how I had tried to play by the rules, participating in the games of the pharmaceutical industry and academic medicine for many years before I realized that it was corrupt. How Roche attacked me, and humiliated me. Stripped away everything I had worked for, ruined my career, and made me feel like that little boy in the laundry room with the wet pants.

I told her about my journey to learn more about my mother and her family. "Finding my mother's biological family didn't fill in the missing pieces of the puzzle. I feel like my mother is still calling me, still has something for me to do, but I don't know what it is."

"At some point, it will be good for you to stand up to your father, to tell him that you have issues with the way things went in your childhood. How he dealt with your mother and not letting you grieve."

"I don't think I can do that." The thought alone terrified me.

"Did your parents ever take you to your mother's grave?"

"She didn't have a grave. She was cremated."

"What happened to her ashes?"

"Well... I don't know... I don't think there were any ashes left over after she was cremated."

"There are always remains after a cremation. It's not possible to completely get rid of the remains."

"I have a vague memory of hearing something about how her ashes were spread over Lake Chelan in Washington state. And my sister also said that she thought she was 'absolutely cremated,' meaning there was nothing left after she died."

"It's not possible to absolutely cremate someone."

"Maybe I should ask my father about it then." That was not a happy thought.

"How're things going at home?"

"My 17-year-old daughter hates me. My wife says that I'm acting like my stepmother. She sides with my daughter against me. I feel trapped and isolated and fantasize about escaping." I looked out the plate-glass window at the forest of green.

"Tell me more about that."

"When I was five years old, shortly after the death of my mother, I was walking through the streets of Seattle with my parents. They turned into a department store. I kept walking straight ahead, and got lost."

"It doesn't seem like they were paying much attention to you."

"I guess not. Later they said that they were thinking of buying a leash to keep track of me."

"That sounds horrible. What happened to you?"

"I was standing there crying, and someone waved down a cop. He drove me around on his motorcycle. He had these round discs that I held onto. When he found my parents, I was almost reluctant to let go. Years later, we were on a wheat ranch in eastern Oregon that was owned by a friend of my parents. We were out in the barnyard. The other kid was revving a motorcycle. I asked if I could ride it around the barnyard. Once I got on the motorcycle, I just took off. Riding toward the horizon. I had a total sense of freedom."

"What happened next?"

"After half an hour, I didn't know what to do. So I turned around and went back. They were really pissed at me. Later when I was in high school, my main fantasy was to buy a motorcycle after high school and take off. That is what my brother did. But my stepmother said that they would not pay for my college if I did that. They didn't pay much for my college, anyway."

"How does that relate to your life now?"

"My wife and daughter are always accusing me. I feel like I did when I was a child. I fantasize about jumping on a motorcycle and riding away."

"You can't expect your wife to be thrilled with you after your behavior emailing that other woman," she said. "You need to give it some time. I'll see you next week, same time."

I started thinking about what might have happened to my mother's remains. I emailed my father to ask what happened to my mother's ashes. I waited for a response.

## CHAPTER 46

I got a response to the email I wrote to my father about my mother's ashes. He said that he didn't know what happened to her ashes, that was the responsibility of the funeral home, and he had other things on his mind at the time. That made me angry. What the hell was he talking about?

I knew the name of the funeral home because I wrote away for my mother's death certificate the year before. I put in a call to them. They said that she was in the "community crypt." They would have to check on something and get back to me. What the hell was a community crypt? I didn't have my wits about me enough to ask. I would wait until the next day.

When I got the call back, I learned that the "community crypt" was a euphemism for the place they put the people whose ashes never got picked up. The man told me that 20 years ago, when the funeral home underwent a change of ownership, my mother's ashes, which until then had been stored in a closet, had been buried in a common site with the urns of all of the other people whose ashes had never been picked up from the funeral home, hence the term, "community crypt."

When I understood what the situation was, I asked them to dig up the site.

I felt as if I were losing my mind. Between the fraud inquiry at Emory and my mother's ashes not having received a proper burial, it was hard to keep things together.

"You need to call your father and tell him about how you feel about your mother's ashes," my wife told me.

"I know. My psychiatrist told me that I should stand up to him. But the thought of confronting him makes me feel physically ill." I felt like I wanted to throw up. I lay on my side on the ground, and tried to get myself together.

"You need to make the call."

I walked outside. I made the call on my cell phone. He didn't pick up, so I left a message. I felt nauseous. I retched, but nothing came out. I walked back into the house and lay down on my side again, panting. After 20 minutes, my cell phone rang.

"There's something I wanted to talk to you about." I took a deep breath. "I found out that my mother's ashes were buried in a common burial site because you never picked her up from the funeral home."

"She never asked to be picked up from the funeral home," he said defensively. "She only asked to be cremated, and never made any specifications about what should be done after that. I only did what she asked me to do."

"But they wrote you a letter 20 years ago, when I was 21 years old and was perfectly able to add my opinion about the situation, asking you to come pick up her ashes, and you said that she should be put in the 'community crypt,' which meant that her ashes were buried with the ashes of the other people whose families never came to pick them up, or the people who had no families or anyone else to care about them. I certainly don't count myself in the list of people who didn't care about the remains of my mother. I resent the fact that you didn't ask my input about it, since I was an adult when they contacted you about the community crypt."

"I don't have any memory of that."

"So do you deny that you signed that letter?"

"I don't deny it. That was a long time ago."

"I also resent the fact that I never had any pictures of my mother, and that I wasn't allowed to grieve—"

"—what are you talking about," he interrupted.

"We weren't allowed to talk about it."

"We never stopped talking about it."

"And Charlie—"

"—what about Charlie—"

"—you shouldn't have made me give him up right after my mother died—"

Charlie was my dog, a black-haired Standard Poodle. After my mother died and my father remarried they gave him to the housekeeper. They said I could visit him whenever I wanted to, but I only saw him once more in my life. I hadn't thought about Charlie in many years. The thought just sort of popped into my head.

"—-he pooped all over the place. I'm here with grandma," he went on, "who is very sick. I can't deal with this crap." The mother of my stepmother was 100 years old, and at the end of her life.

"I'm sorry. I wish this came up at a better time."

"If you were so interested in her, why didn't you come pick up her ashes?"

"--I was only five years old at the time--"

"—-and when you were 21?"

"I don't know. I didn't know about her ashes then. It took me awhile to learn about what happened. You said that you learned after her death that she may have been having an affair. Do you think that you may have been angry at her?"

"Why would I be angry at her? She was dead!"

"Dad, I'm a psychiatrist, and for you to say that you cannot be angry at someone who is dead, that's just plain false."

"Now you're trying to take something and twist it around-—"

"—-no I'm not-—"

"--saying I was angry at Laurnell—-"

"-—I didn't say that. I was just asking a question."

"I want you to apologize for the fact that you made these accusations against me—-"

"—-what do you mean, apologize—-"

"--You need to apologize to me—-"

"For what?"

"Right now. For accusing me of not picking up her ashes because I was angry at her."

I didn't know what to say. "I'm sorry for bringing up the fact that you may have been angry at my mother for possible infidelities, in conjunction with mentioning that you didn't pick up her ashes at the funeral home."

"You accused me of being angry at Laurnell, and I want you to take it back. I demand an apology." Nice game, get angry and blame me.

"As I said before, I'm sorry I brought up the topic of my mother's supposed infidelities in connection with the issue of my mother's ashes, and I apologize for that." This went on for several rounds. I didn't think that we were going to get anywhere with this.

"I'm not letting you off the phone until you apologize to me."

"I have to go to work now, Dad. I have to hang up now."

"I'm not hanging up until this is resolved. I am worried about how this will affect our relationship."

"Goodbye, Dad. I have to go to work now."

"Are you coming to see us at Christmas?"

I paused. How could he bring that up now? "We're going to Italy," I lied.

"You always go to Italy. You never come here at Christmas."

"I've got to go to work now. Goodbye." With that, I hung up the phone.

"How did it go?" my wife asked me.

"I don't know. I said what I had to say. Did I sound like I was being reasonable?"

"Yes, you were fine."

"He was like a lunatic."

"Don't worry. Things will be fine."

# CHAPTER 47

Later that night, I was sitting out on the back patio of our home in Atlanta. The night air was warm and heavy. Fireflies arced and flitted about over the dark green lawn, beneath the giant magnolia tree. Its scented white flowers and dark green leaves glittered in the moonlight.

I called my older sister, Lynn, on my Blackberry. "I did some research and found out that our mother is buried in an unmarked site. She's in a space with 40 other people who were cremated and whose remains were never reclaimed by their families."

"That's terrible."

"They're digging up the site as we speak. The urns are marked, so we should be able to get her back, which raises the question of what we should do with her."

"Why don't we have her ashes spread over the Nisqually River? She was involved with the coalition to save the river delta from the early days."

"It's weird. I always had the idea that her ashes were spread over Lake Chelan."

"Someone told me that there was nothing left after she was cremated."

"That's not possible. There's always something left."

Or at least that is what my psychiatrist told me.

## CHAPTER 48

I got a call back from the funeral home. They had dug up the urns, but the labeling had degenerated to such a degree that they could not identify which one belonged to my mother. A sickening feeling came over me. I called my sister again.

"What did you have them do?"

"I asked them to cover up the site again," I said.

"I can't believe this is happening." I felt the same way.

"I think we should buy a tombstone to put over the site."

"I can buy a tombstone the next time I go to Olympia."

"I don't know. I feel more comfortable getting one myself." After all of the screw-ups, including the possible failings of medical care that I suspected may have taken away my mother, and the failure to pick her up from the funeral home and give her a proper burial, I didn't want to leave this in anyone else's hands. I wanted to make sure it was done right this time. "It's too bad that her four-year-old boy has to be the one to buy her tombstone for her, 40 years later."

I looked around on the Internet for a tombstone. How did one go about these things? How was I supposed to know? The only funeral I ever went to was when I was 10 years old. It was for a great uncle that I had only met twice. Now I had to find a tombstone for my mother who died 40 years ago? I couldn't find anything on the Internet. Didn't everyone have to die at some point? You'd think that there should be a pretty stable market for tombstones. I drove out to one place. It was closed. I was confused. I felt lost. I went down to the next one on the list. It was way on the other side of town. I finally found the place, surrounded by acres and acres of tombstones and cemetery.

"Can I help you?" the man behind the counter said.

"I need to buy a tombstone. Can you ship it to Washington state?"

"Sure. Any idea of what you have in mind?"

"Not really. I don't have a lot of experience with this sort of thing. Something simple, in plain granite, I guess. Set in the ground. I better go over it with my siblings as well."

"Here are some examples of different types of engravings and styles of headstones. Why don't you email me and then we can send you a version to preview."

I went home and picked out a couple of possibilities and emailed them to my siblings. We picked out a design, and soon the memorial company was carving a tombstone to be shipped across the country for my mother's funeral. I called the funeral home and made arrangements for a ceremony to be held on October 4, 2008, when the tombstone would be placed in the ground, hopefully with all her family present. I planned a party to be held afterward and made up invitations that I sent to everyone who knew her, as well as others who didn't, like the cousins of her half sister, Ellie. I next went to a Web site for a flower shop in Olympia. Through tears, I picked out the flowers for my mother's belated funeral. Each type of flower had a different meaning: Bouvardia for enthusiasm, gladiolus for strength of character, statice for remembrance, a dozen roses for love, sunflowers for pure thoughts, lisianthus for charisma and confidence, and birds of paradise for joyfulness.

I had written the history of my father's side of the family, and researched their family tree, having inherited all the old family charts and letters about the history of our family from my grandfather. I decided now was the time to write the history of my mother. I called a woman named Jeanne Turnbow, whom I knew was one of her friends, but whom I had never talked to before.

"Doug," she said. "I can't believe it. After all these years." I updated her on my life.

"Your mother was a wonderful woman. She was involved in a number of political and environmental causes. She was always sewing something or cooking something that smelled good."

"Thanks for sharing that with me."

"She had her own unique sayings. I am trying to remember them."

Jeanne gave me the names of some other people who were my mother's friends. I looked them up online. Many of them were part of a group in the Unitarian church, called the Unitarian Fellowship of Olympia, or UFO, appropriately enough, as they seemed like a colorful group of people inspired by the spirit of the 1960s. Some were still alive; others were not.

I called a woman named Lois that Jeanne described as one of my mother's closest friends.

"She died so suddenly," Lois said. "It was such a shock to all of us. And then your father remarried only three months later. They moved away almost immediately. Your father completely cut us off. We didn't have any answers to our questions about what happened to her.

"I'm sorry we couldn't have done more for you kids. One of our friends tried to bring food over for a while, but it was clear that she wasn't welcome."

"Did you ever hear anything about her having an affair?"

"No. I don't know how she would have time. She had four little kids. She used to shuttle you around in her Paul Volkswagen convertible. She was so proud of you. And of her car! You were in my pre-school class at the cooperative. Do you remember?"

"I do remember!" I said. I felt the memory coming back to me. The pre-school was a safe place for me after my mother died. Now I knew why.

"When it was her turn to teach, she was nice to all the children, but you were always given special priority. You used to like your sandwich made a special way."

"And how was that?"

"Peanut butter and onion, on toast. But the onion had to be peeled a special way. And only she could do it right."

I cried silently to myself. I couldn't say anything for a moment. "I'm sorry; I'm overcome with emotion."

"That's OK. I probably shouldn't tell you this, but my son died at exactly the same age as my husband, 54, and now I'm raising my grandson, who's in high school, and I'm 84 years old."

"I'm sorry to hear that."

"My husband had a chronic illness, and spent his later years in bed. After he died, I didn't show him to my grandson. I think that was a mistake, because, being a boy, he thought he was still in the room, living under the bed."

"Children have the right to know."

"Well, life can be hard sometimes. I hope you find what you're looking for."

"I'm not sure if I know what that is, but I think I'm going in the right direction. Or I hope so, anyway."

"I'm sure you are."

I talked with more of her friends. I was able to figure out that I hadn't been at the ceremony held for her by the local Unitarian fellowship group, which explained why I now felt the need for a funeral. One of them had an actual transcript of what was said at the ceremony, I was thrilled to discover, and had kept it all these years. She sent me a copy in the mail. One of them said that they asked a psychic what happened to my mother. The psychic asked what medications she was on, and said that one of them could cause meningitis.

Through the Internet I was able to get into contact with the kids of my mother's friends, some of whom we had been friends with so long ago in the old Fishtrap neighborhood where we lived on Puget Sound before my mother died. One was a graduate student of divinity at Harvard who was interested in the study of emotion and spirituality. She called me "Fishtrap Frere." I told her that I was a researcher who was now focusing on the study of emotion. With a sample size of one.

"I remember your mother wearing a very chic Paul dress," she said. "She looked like Jackie Onassis. Very fashionable but Bohemian at the same time. I know she was involved in a number of political causes, like fighting for the environment or against the Vietnam War."

"I heard she was friends with Giovanni Costigan, a famous historian at the University of Washington," I said. "I read that he was a famous political liberal who had a debate with William F. Buckley that had more people in the audience than the Seattle Supersonics game that was playing that night."

"The Supersonics weren't that great in those days, anyway."

"Laugh out loud!"

"I remember her sitting in the kitchen of her house, and us little kids were running all around, and she would be decked out in pearls and smoking a pipe full of cigarette butts. Very *au contraire*, very Bohemian. She was the spirit of the age. The 1960s. Things were changing then."

"It looks like their little social group, the Unitarian fellowship group, kind of imploded after she died."

"Yes, well, things didn't go well for my family. And a lot of the other ones had some collateral damage from the experimentation of the 60s."

"I know. Thanks a lot for talking to me. I really appreciate it." And I really did.

I had gathered enough information. Now it was time to write the story of my mother. I drove to a coffee shop in the Oakhurst neighborhood called Kavarna. I opened my laptop and started to write the HTML code to create a Web site for my mother. It was nestled within www.Bremnerhistory.com, the original one I made to post the history of my family, which up until then had a glaring absence in one of its halves. I uploaded all of the pictures that I had of her as well as the transcript of her memorial.

It was hard going, my eyes were full of tears, and I couldn't shake the old feeling that I shouldn't be doing this, that I was going to Violate a taboo. I looked around the coffee shop. The other people were all focused on their laptops, or lost in conversation. It didn't seem like anyone had noticed that I was crying. I pushed on. I made links to her friends, both dead and alive, and wrote the history of her life. I tried to remember everything I could from the time when she was still alive and write it down.

I remembered the wind blowing through the leaves of the madrona tree at our house on a bluff overlooking Puget Sound. The peeling red bark. Sitting on the beach with a playmate, putting sand in a bottle and then eating it. Dancing with my teddy bear to the song, "I want to hold your hand." Scooting around on my bottom (I never learned to crawl). My mother limping around the house, carrying me on her hip. The museum where she volunteered and we had a Christmas party for all of the little children. Her look of joy when I came into the room. The day she was taken away and never came back. Did I do something wrong that made my Mommy leave me? Could I go to the place where she was at?

My heart hurt as I wrote the words. But I kept on. I finished the Web site. That was done.

Later that day, I thought about what my mother's friends had told me. One of the things bothering me was that her best friend didn't know that she had been having an affair when she died. Maybe my father was lying to me? The story had been that my aunt, Jane, came down to the house after my mother died and took all of her clothes, and had found some notes in the pocket of her coat that were like notes you would write to someone to arrange a tryst. But that could be just like some of the other stories that had floated around among us children, that her ashes were spread over Lake Chelan, or that she was descended from a Laplander. Stories we shared and cherished, but were too frightened to ask about in the open. I decided now was the time to make the call and find out the truth.

"Your father asked me to come down and get her clothes," she said. "We were the same size, so they all fit me perfectly, and I guess he just wanted to get any reminders of her out of the house. I found some notes in the pocket of her coat that were like the kind that lovers would write to each other to arrange meetings."

"What did they say?"

"Oh, nothing exciting. Just let's meet here at such and such a time, kind of thing."

"Are you sure that they were notes that people would exchange who were having an affair?"

"Yes, I'm sure."

"Did you tell my father about them?"

"No, I didn't feel comfortable telling him about it. They asked to meet with us a month after your mother died. They said that she had been having an affair when she died."

"That's interesting," I said. "I wonder how he found out? He wasn't the type to go riffling through her clothes."

My uncle, my father's brother, was on the line now. "So how has all of this been for you?"

"It's been great to talk to all of the people who knew her, and to find out what a wonderful person she really was. I spent so many years shutting her out of my heart. I didn't want to think about her. Now after all these years, I feel like I'm getting in touch with her again, that her spirit is entering my heart." I stopped. "I'm sorry, but I am having trouble talking." I felt overwhelmed with grief. Tears streamed down my cheeks.

"I'm glad that you have found her again," Jane said. "She'll be a source of strength for you."

I paused. I watched the silhouette of the trees against the evening Georgia skyline. The fireflies were carrying on their mating games, hovering above the grass in the sweltering Georgia night.

"I hope so," I said. "I'm going to need it."

\* \* \*

My funeral arrangements were interrupted by a call from my father telling me that my stepmother's

mother had died. The funeral was in three days. I felt
torn. I didn't want to tell him about the ceremony for
my mother yet. I wanted to focus on planning the
ceremony, without other distractions. I felt she
deserved that, after all these years. But I also thought
that going to my stepmother's mother's funeral was the
right thing to do. I decided to go.

# CHAPTER 49

That night, I took the dog out for a walk at 11:00 p.m. My wife had already gone up to bed. We crossed busy Ponce de Leon Avenue to Deepdene Park.

The park had a large field with a line of trees around the perimeter that they called The Mead. Beyond that was a wild part with a forest of trees and a little stream meandering through the midst called The Vale. I listened to music by Death Cab for Cutie on my Treo.

*The Atlantic was born today and I'll tell you how:*
*The clouds above opened up, and let it out.*
*I was standing on the surface of a perforated*
sphere
*When the water, filled every hole,*
*And thousands upon thousands made an ocean,*
*Making islands where no island should go,*
*Oh no*

*Those people were overjoyed; they took to their*
boats.
*I thought it less like a lake and more like a moat.*
*The rhythm of my footsteps crossing flood lands to*
*your door have been silenced forever more.*
*The distance is quite simply much too far for me to*
row,
*It seems farther than ever before,*
*Oh no.*

*I need you so much closer*
*I need you so much closer*
*I need you so much closer*
*I need you so much closer*

I looked at the outline of the trees against the night skyline. I realized they were all leaf trees, hickory, oak, and tuliptree, just like the trees in the dream I had of my mother when I was a little child. But we didn't have forests of leaf trees in Washington state where I grew up. They were all fir trees, evergreens, with pine needles.

I suddenly realized that the forest of my dreams was here, right across the street from my house, in Atlanta.

She came to me in my dreams, to foreshadow a place where I would see her again. It felt surreal. And then I remembered how angry I had been at her for leaving me alone. I remembered feeling like I must have been a very bad boy indeed for having a Mommy who left me like that. I felt the full weight of the shame and guilt I felt after her death. I remembered the person with two faces that I had become, trying to hide the inner wounds. And she was with me here, right now. I could feel her presence. Looking at me.

I stared at the jagged tree line that meandered against the night sky. I cried for a long time.

I'm sorry I forgot about you, I told my mother.

My body was filled with grief, and yet, maybe for the first time in years, I felt fully alive.

# CHAPTER 50

With all of the activity related to my mother, I almost forgot about my anniversary with my wife. But my wife remembered and made reservations for dinner at a restaurant on the Chattahoochee River. We got in the car to go to the restaurant. My cell phone rang. It was my sister, Lynn. My wife scowled at me. Lynn asked me about the arrangements for the ceremony.

"The tombstone is being shipped out to Olympia as we speak. I was kind of worried that it might rain. Do you think we should rent some tents for the party?"

"I don't know. Maybe we should just bring a bunch of umbrellas."

The conversation went on for most of the drive up to the restaurant. When I got off the phone, my wife said, "This is our anniversary. Can't you stop thinking about your mother for a while?"

"I know, I know." My daughter had recently said the same thing. "Why don't you pay some attention to the living?"

We were seated at our table. It was outdoors with a large lawn stretching in front of us, and the Chattahoochee River at the end of the lawn. It flowed by silently, always moving but always in one place. I wondered where its waters came from, and where they were going. Fireflies flickered up on the lawn, and then fell down. They were following through on the ancient mating rituals of times past. The females waited on a blade of grass, and the males flew through the air, flashing. When the females saw a flashing pattern that they liked, they would flash at the males, who flew down to mate with them. I wondered how my parents met. I didn't think that I could ask my father.

"I got the transcript of the memorial for my mother. Someone had kept it all these years. Isn't that amazing? I don't think that anyone knew it existed. Can I read it to you?"

"OK."

Straining under the light of a candle, I read to her. "'When Laurnell walked into a room, it was like a light bulb was turned on.' Nice imagery, don't you think?"

"Yes, that is nice. But this is our anniversary. Can't we talk about us?"

"But if I don't understand my feelings about my mother, and the past, I won't be able to be available for you and the kids as much as I should."

Just then, the wind picked up in the upper branches of the trees over the Chattahoochee.

"I feel like the spirit of my mother is with us here now," I said.

"I spent a lot of time to find a nice restaurant for our anniversary," my wife said, exasperated. "Why doesn't your mother tell you to focus your attention on your family."

As we drove home I played a song over and over in my mind about a place where no cars go.

The dilemma of being with my family was still in my mind. It was hard when I was spending so much time grieving for my mother, after being emotionally dead for all these years. I knew I had to grieve to change, but it just made me feel as if I wanted to be alone. I didn't have an answer for my dilemma.

I didn't have much time to think about these questions. I had to catch a flight to Seattle in the morning to attend the funeral. I was worried that a combustible situation would explode, but we can't always control the future. Or the past, either, for that matter.

# CHAPTER 51

I checked in to the Avis counter at Seattle-Tacoma International Airport. Turning my rental SUV onto I-5 South to Olympia, I got a call on my cell phone.

"When are you coming in?" my father asked me.

"About 7 p.m. I have a hotel room reserved downtown."

"You don't need to stay in a hotel. Why don't you stay with us?" I wanted to have my own room, so that if things went south, I would have an escape route. Besides, I had already put the deposit on the hotel room, so not staying there was just a waste of money. My ever-present desire to please overrode everything else, however, and against my better instincts, I agreed.

On the way down to Olympia, I picked up a dozen roses. I drove out to the cemetery. They had told me what part of the cemetery my mother was buried in, and I could identify the site because it had been recently dug up. It was nighttime, and no one was there. There was a light mist falling. The evergreen trees crowded around. I thought about how many times I had driven by this place, and never knew she was there. I placed the flowers on the site.

I was a swirl of emotions. Sadness, at the loss of my mother, which made my heart hurt. Regret that she couldn't spend time with her grandkids, as I know she would have loved to do. Pride, for having found her, after all these years, and for having fought for her.

Next, I went out to the house where we lived
while my mother was still alive. It was the first time I
had ever gone back since the time we moved away
when I was five years old. I wondered why I never went
during my high school and college years, when I could
have driven there myself without telling anyone.

I wasn't sure where the house was, exactly. I
drove into the center of town, and then continued along
the road that ran along the east side of the bay. I
followed my instincts. The road plunged through the
forest of Priest Point Park. This was where my
grandfather brought us to cut sling-shots out of maple
branches after my mother died. A way to fill up our
time. After I left the park, the road came to a branch.
Directly ahead was a beautiful farm with rolling hills of
cow pasture surrounded by Douglas fir trees. I
recognized it from my childhood, and turned to the
right along Libby Road. Now the trees towered above,
and I could see glimpses of the blue waters of the sound
off to the right. I reached Fish Trap Road, and slowed
down. I couldn't recognize which one was the house.

After going down one or two driveways, I found
one that looked familiar. I parked the car at the head of
the gravel driveway and walked toward the house. I
realized that this was the one.

It was a lovely house built in a Japanese style on
a bluff overlooking Puget Sound. The house was dark
and empty; no one was home. What once had been a
wild piece of land in the back full of fallen trees had
now been turned into a tidy farm, with an apple
orchard, vegetable garden, grape vines, and three
sheep, who stood silently, gazing at me. My mother had

been a Buddhist, and since the Buddhists believe in reincarnation, I wondered if she had come back as a sheep, to live another lifetime in that place she had loved, after her first one was interrupted.

I got back into the rental car, and drove away with my thoughts.

When I arrived at my parents' house, I found a note saying they had gone out to dinner. I packed a bottle of Dewar's scotch in my suit case for the trip, since I didn't know how they might react to my dipping into their bar. I pulled the bottle out and got a glass and some ice and poured myself a drink. I walked down to the porch of the main house that overlooked Puget Sound. It was a clear night. The water was like a dark sheet of glass. The sky was clear and there was a full moon. I relaxed and drank my scotch.

After about an hour, they arrived. They found me on the patio.

"Looks like you travel prepared," my stepmother said, looking at the scotch.

"Don't want to be a burden."

"So what's up with this thing with Laurnell?" my father asked with a friendly look that had a tinge of apprehension.

"I wanted to buy a tombstone to put over the site where she was buried. I don't think it was right that she was buried in an unmarked spot."

"I had nothing to do with that," my stepmother said. "That was your father's doing."

"She never said that she wanted to be buried," my father said, getting defensive.

"I've been doing some research on Laurnell." I felt a quelling feeling in my stomach. I took a sip of the wine they had just poured for me. "I've been calling all of her old friends. Like Joan Turner and Lori Benson." *The play's the thing.*

My father looked astonished. "How did you know about them?"

"Really? Tell us about it," my stepmother said. "What did you find out?"

"You'd be surprised. Some of your old friends wondered why you got married only three months after my mother's death." I watched them carefully. I was having trouble reading them.

"I had four little kids to take care of," my father said. "I had to do something. Who was going to take care of you kids?"

"They were wondering why you started dating so soon after Laurnell's death. I wanted to find out how you met. Lori said that you were working together at the mental health clinic and that you knew each other before my mother died."

"Laurnell was the head of the Mental Health Board for the county," my stepmother said. "I worked under her as a mental health worker for the county. It was well known that she had affairs with other men."

"Like who?"

"Well, Walter Buckley, for one. He was a leading figure in the Democratic Party in Washington state."

"And did the two of you have a relationship with each other before my mother died?"

"Of course not," my stepmother said. "Those aren't my morals."

"Why are you so focused on this now?" he asked.

"Finding her ashes made me wonder how many other things I didn't know." My parents looked at each other.

"Laurnell was no good for you kids," my father said. "She wasn't a good mother. You're better off without her."

"I've heard you say that before." I tried to turn the conversation in another direction. I didn't want to ruin things right before the funeral of my stepmother's mother. I felt apprehensive, but it was also good to get things out in the open for once.

# CHAPTER 52

As I sat in the Catholic Church during the service for my stepmother's mother, I watched my father out of the corner of my eye mumbling prayers in response to the priest. Was this the same man who got angry at me for reading the Bible when I was in high school? In retrospect, of course, I realized that I was reading that particular Bible because it was the only possession I had that came from my mother. And maybe that was why he got angry at me for reading it. Who knows?

As the priest read the service, I cried. I didn't know if I was crying for the mother of my stepmother, my mother, or myself. After the ceremony, we walked out into the bright sunshine, and then drove out to the cemetery. I remembered that this was the same cemetery where my brother had said there was a headstone for my mother. There were thousands of headstones there now, so I had no way of verifying that. Probably just another one of those myths we shared as kids.

We gathered around a deep hole in the ground with a casket next to it. Four men lowered the casket into the ground. One took a shovel and threw some dirt on the casket. *So that is how it was done*, I thought.

Afterwards, we went to the home of my stepmother's mother. My stepmother's sister lived in an adjacent condo. Her husband had died a couple of years before, and she had married a man whose wife had also died. They had pictures of themselves on the wall with their deceased spouses next to them. She still kept the ashes of her deceased husband in a closet in the house.

My stepmother and her sister went through their mother's things. Here was a favorite picture. And some notes she had written to their father.

I surreptitiously walked over to a bulletin board that was full of photographs, mostly of her biological grandchildren. There was one photo of my siblings and me from about 30 years ago sitting on a couch, ranging in age from me at age 12, my older sisters 15 and 17, and my brother age 18, with two baby cousins sitting on the floor. On the back was written "Bremners-4" along with the names of the two baby cousins. I slipped it into my pocket. I would keep that as a memento.

I asked my parents questions about the time when my mother was still alive. My stepmother knew her then. I was curious. But asking about the past turned out to be a mistake. As was my decision not to stay in my own hotel room.

# CHAPTER 53

We walked back to my parents' house, which was just down the road. The evergreen fir trees stood fiercely on either side of the road. The blackness sat in front. A misty rain began to ooze from the silent skies.

You had to go through the garage to get into the house. Two brand new Mercedes Benzes glittered in the artificial light, metallic. A freezer stuffed with dead meat waited nearby.

Once we got inside the house, I regretted having talked about the past earlier in the day.

"When're you ever going to get over this?" my father asked. "This is the woman who raised you, right here." He pointed at my stepmother.

"You were always so *angry* as a child," my stepmother said. "What do you have against me?"

"I don't have anything against you. This isn't about you. This is about me. I'm doing this for myself and my kids. I don't think it's right that you put my mother down and that we didn't have any pictures of her, or that we weren't allowed to grieve for her."

"We never stopped talking about her," my father said.

"That isn't my memory of what happened."
"You weren't grateful to this one who raised you," he shouted, pointing at my stepmother again.
"This isn't against mom. I'm just saying that your telling us to just get over it was not the best way to help us grieve the loss of our mother."

"It was the best way," my father said.

"No, it wasn't. What do you base your comments on?"

"Based on what I say. I am a psychiatrist."

"So am I." Battle of the psychiatrists. "And I've reviewed the literature on the topic, and the consensus does not support your views."

"I don't care what the consensus says. I know what's important. You need to move on and not dwell on the past."

"I disagree with you. And the consensus of the field does not agree with you either."

"Well, you're wrong."

"You're the one who's wrong."

My sister came downstairs. "I can't believe you're doing this, on this day of all days, when we buried grandma."

"You need to move on and get over the past," my father said.

"I don't think we're going to go anywhere on this topic—-" "--we're not finished yet—"

"--It's late. I think we should go to bed--"

"--You're going to stay here until we're done."

"You've had a long day with the funeral and everything," I moved toward the door.

"We're not finished. You can't leave."

"This probably isn't the best time to talk about this. I have nothing else to say." I went outside. An angry black sky swirled with clouds. It hovered above the house. Fluid slid off Douglas Firs that towered like angry giants above my head.

I went up to my room in the guest house. My flight was at six a.m. It didn't make sense to sleep, even if I was able to. I lay on my bed for an hour. Finally, I got up and threw up in the bathroom. The bile left an acid taste in my mouth. I put a copy of the book I had been reading about children and bereavement, *Never Too Young to Know,* in their mailbox. It had the references to the literature I was talking about, and I didn't need it any more. I got in my rental car and drove out to the house on Steamboat Island Road, where we were going to have the party. Coming off the freeway, I saw the neon lights of a package store blinking like the face of a clown. I turned into the long, silent corridor that ran between the evergreen trees. Steamboat Island Road. It was an empty place. Grey sky and a strip of black asphalt that glistened in the rain and ran like a straight arrow into the infinite universe. The only sound was the swishing of the windshield wipers. It seemed like I drove forever. Finally, I arrived at the house and got out of the car. It was on a bluff with a steep cliff that fell down to the beach, just like our old house in the place we called Fishtrap where we lived when my mother was still alive. I got out of the car. The sky was cold and peaceful. This would be a good place for the party we planned to celebrate my mother's life.

I drove back to the cemetery again and walked to my mother's grave site in the rain. It was about three in the morning. I stood over her, full of feelings. Anger, regret, sadness. I pulled out my wallet and found pictures of my two kids. I placed them over her.

"You would have been so proud of them," I said out loud. I cried. I don't know when I stopped. When I did, I got into the rental car and drove toward the Seattle airport.

The Thunderbird flew across the sky from the great ocean to the west.

# CHAPTER 54

"My father made me promise to tell you that he thinks I'm bipolar and need to be on medication." I was back in Dr. S.'s office again. He called me on my cell phone when I was driving home from the Atlanta airport. He demanded to talk to my psychiatrist, but I refused. The only way I could get him off the phone was to promise him that I would pass along his opinions to my psychiatrist.

"What do you think?"

"I don't think I need medication. I think that they're just angry at me because I brought up the subject of my mother at the funeral of my stepmother's mother."

"That probably wasn't the best time to bring it up."

"I know. I had to tell them sometime. I would have felt uncomfortable going to Olympia for the ceremony without them knowing that I was there. It's a small town. What if I ran into someone who knew them?"

"You could have told them on the phone."

"I guess I was being a bit selfish. But there were so many questions about the circumstances of her death, like the fact that she contracted a type of bacterial meningitis that is usually never seen in adults, and the fact that he started dating right away, and married three months later."

"Do you think he may have had some responsibility for her death?" she asked.

"I don't know. I have thought about the possibility. If he didn't love her anymore, maybe he didn't try as hard as he might otherwise have to save her life."

I told her about the psychic saying that her death was caused by a prescription medication. I looked it up and, sure enough, there was a disorder called aseptic meningitis that could be triggered by certain antibiotics and pain medications. From her death certificate, I learned that she had pneumonia preceding the bacterial meningitis. Her friends said that she looked sick the week before she died. My father was a doctor. Why hadn't he done something for her?

"Maybe she took an antibiotic or pain medication that triggered the meningitis? Even though I'm a doctor, my father never gave me the full medical history, and I was always afraid to ask. That's why I wanted to talk about it with them in person, to see the reaction on their faces when I told them about the details I had learned about my mother's death, to see if there was something they weren't telling me. 'The play's the thing wherein I'll catch the conscience of the king.'"

"Hamlet," she said.

"That's right."

"Hamlet's mother remarried three months after his father died. Just like your father."

"'Funeral baked meats, set forth for the marriage feast.' The European royalty felt that it was a sin against nature to marry less than a year after the death of a spouse."

"What do you think?"

"My mother was a Buddhist, and they believe in karma, or the idea that your actions will eventually come back to you, for good or evil, in this life or the next. Which is what Shakespeare meant I guess when he made the ghost of Hamlet's father say, 'As to your mother, Hamlet, leave her to heaven.'"

"Hamlet's uncle killed his father," she said. "How did it make you feel when you thought about the possibility that your father may have born some responsibility for your mother's death?"

"Not good." It actually felt much worse than that. "It's bad enough that I had her taken away from me and was left in a cesspool of grief. If he had some responsibility, that would be more than I could bear."

"You, Doug, are Hamlet."

"Yes, I guess I am." I had to stop. My throat was closing. I looked out the plate-glass window. There was a pause. And then I continued.

"The parallels are amazing. I have an impossible conflict, to choose between my mother and my father, just like Hamlet. I felt like I had to deny my mother to retain the love of my father."

"No one should have to be put in that situation."

I paused again. "But at the end of the story, Hamlet dies, and all is lost. The Kingdom of Denmark is wiped clean so that a new generation can start anew. Fortinbras comes from Norway to start a new kingdom."

"I don't think that life has to end like a Shakespearean tragedy, Doug," she said. "Well, that's all the time we have for today."

# CHAPTER 55

The week after the disastrous trip back to Olympia, I was back on an airplane to the South of France. I was scheduled to give a talk in front of the French Society of Psychiatrists at a resort in the hills near the town of Saint Paul de Vence. After being deposited by a taxi at the resort, I decided to walk to the town. The town was a lot farther away than I thought, but I enjoyed the long walk through the hills, the winding roads, gnarled olive trees and stone fences.

When I arrived at the town, I found a delightful small walled city with a labyrinth of interesting alleys and byways. Its charms persisted in spite of the phalanxes of French tourists that periodically discharged from buses. I relished the languorous lifestyle of the South of France, the feeling of a place that shared the timeless culture of the Mediterranean that I had seen in my wife's native Sicily, as well as Greece, Croatia, and other places.

Back at the hotel, I sat in the little private patio outside my room. I thought about how nice it would have been to take my mother along with me on this trip. I'm sure she would have loved it, and the French people would have loved her as well. More than one person had commented to me about the resemblance between her and Jacqueline Onassis, who had a love of French culture. I wouldn't be surprised if she had identified with her.

I thought about the upcoming ceremony, and thought it would be a good idea to write something to say there. And so I got a piece of paper and pen and wrote the following lines:

"As I write this, I am sitting outside my room at Le Mas D'Artigny in the Cote d'Azur in France. I say this because I am sure you would have liked this place, you would have liked France, *bon vivant*, good living, and I would have liked to have the chance to visit it with you. And I think you would have been proud that my accomplishments have taken me to places like France, and England, and many other places. I think you would have been proud of me and my siblings and our children, what we have seen and done and experienced. There are many things I wish you would have seen and done with us. I wish you had seen my graduations, my wedding, gotten to know my wife (I know you would have liked her), and had seen my children being born and growing up. I wish you could have lived to learn who your biological family was, for good or bad, and so I found out who they were for you, since I know that you would have done that yourself had you lived. I wish you could have seen what happened to me, and to my brother and sisters, and their children, and your biological and adoptive families, and so I made a photo composite for you, sort of a composite of all the things you would have seen and experienced and the family who loves you. It is amazing how many things came out of your life, and how many people still remember you with such fondness. I also brought a copy of the memorial service; you had such an amazing impact on so many people.

But there is one part of that service that I disagree with. That your passing should sit lightly on those you left behind. That is not dealing squarely with the truth, and I don't think you would have wanted anything else but the truth. Your passing had a tremendous impact on your children and many others, for many years, up until the present. There is not a day that goes by that I do not think of you. In many ways, I feel that you were calling me to come find you, and so that is why we are here today, because you are not forgotten, and never will be. We are here today because we love you, and we will carry you in our hearts every day of our lives. We have felt grief for you; may you also give us some of your *joie de vivre*, and to our children, and their children's children.

"Your loving son,

"Doug"

I set my pen down, and cried.

One week later, I was back on a plane to Seattle.

# CHAPTER 56

We came to Olympia from the north. There was a large storm on the way. The local Native Americans knew a giant mythical creature, the Thunderbird, who flew in from the Western Ocean, bringing rain and lightening and creating thunderous noises with the beating of his wings. The Thunderbird Motel, which had since burned down, was right across the street from the cemetery where my mother was buried. I remembered.

When we got to town, the wind swirled the rain around in circles. Was the Thunderbird flying across the sky? Did the members of the spirit world herald our arrival? Was the spirit of our mother moved that her children had all come back to be with her and honor her together, after she had been alone in the cold, wet ground, for so many years?

My cell phone caller ID showed an incoming call from my sister, Lynn. "I'm out at the house on Steamboat Island. Do you think we have enough alcohol for the party tomorrow?"

"I picked up a fifth each of scotch, vodka, rum and gin. Plus a case of wine. So I think we should be all set. How're we doing for food?"

"Both me and Vinnie are cooking." This would be the first time I ever met my mother's adoptive sister.

"OK. We'll be there in about an hour."

When we got to the house, I gave Vinnie a hug. She was a white-haired woman in her 70s. My sister,

Lynn, who lived on the soggy and remote ocean coast of
Washington state, was a reincarnation of one of the
wives of Cape Cod whale boat captains who dotted our
family tree. An Olympia Beer in her hand, she took a
drag on a Lucky Strike.

The morning of the ceremony we had breakfast in
a local dive with Lynn and her husband, Mike. The
wind and rain continued their turbulent dance. It
seemed as if the weather mirrored the emotions we felt.
We drove out to the cemetery.

"Is Anne coming?" I asked.

"She should be here." Lynn called on her cell
phone. "She said that she had been emailing you and
you never responded." The waitress refilled our coffee
cups.

"She asked me to take her off my email list after
she got upset about what I was doing. I did what she
asked me to do. Her emails were probably going into
my spam folder, since I didn't have her in my address
book anymore."

"She's on her way now."

We assembled at the funeral home, my brother
and his kids, Lynn and her daughter. About 20 minutes
after the time set for the ceremony, Anne finally
arrived. We walked out to the burial site. The wind was
blowing so strong it almost whipped our umbrellas
away. I didn't know what we were supposed to do.

A sodden, sturdy-looking man in workman's
clothes approached us. "I was the one who dug up the
site last month. I'm sorry that we couldn't identify the
remains."

"Thanks for your help. I really appreciate it. What're we going to do today?"

"We'll lower the marker over the site." I could see that a piece of ground had been dug out to receive the granite marker, which I was relieved to see was there and ready to be placed in the ground. I guess it had survived its three-thousand-mile trip from Atlanta.

My sister Lynn, I, my son Lucca, and the gravedigger each took hold of one end of two ropes, and lowered the tombstone into the ground. I looked at the marker. It read, "Madeline Laurnell Cooper Bremner, February 23, 1932-February 12, 1966. Beloved mother and grandmother. You are not forgotten."

"I'd like to say a few words." I took out the piece I had written in France. This was it. I filled with emotion. My throat closed. I couldn't speak. Panic. *What if I can't talk?* I thought. *Move forward. Force the words out of your mouth.*

"I am writing this from the South of France..." I could hear the others around me, crying. I relaxed a little. I read a little more. It was going OK now. I reminded myself that all of her children were there. And her grandchildren. Finally, she got the recognition she deserved.

She was there with us. I could feel her spirit. In the trees. This was her place. She was incredibly happy now.

After the ceremony, we stood there for a while under our umbrellas. The wind and the rain died down. We drove back to the house on Steamboat Island. The sun started to peer around the clouds.

"That was great, Doug," Lynn said in the car. "It hit the spot, perfectly."

The son of one of my mother's old friends was at the party. "My father died when I was three years old. After he died, I didn't understand what had happened to him. I thought he was living in an electrical transformer outside of our house. I never could get full closure on his death. It didn't make sense to me that I would be so hung up on it since I was so young when he died. I finally had a ceremony of my own for him. Not all of my siblings came, but most of them did."

"That sounds great." I drank a beer.

"My family was never very good at bringing things to closure."

"I really wish I'd gotten a chance to meet your mother. She was a great friend of my mother's, and I loved the tribute you wrote to her online."

"She kept the urns of the ashes of her relatives in her closet. In one of my psychotherapy sessions after she died, I brought in all of the urns, and we did a family therapy session."

"That's hilarious!" I laughed out loud.

Lynn approached me. "What time is your flight tomorrow?"

"10:00 a.m."

"That's the same time I'm flying to Atlanta for vacation with our parents," my other sister, Anne, said. "We'll be on the same flight."

"That will be awkward." One more thing to worry about.

## CHAPTER 57

We got to the airport the next day, and went through check-in and boarding without seeing my parents.

"I wonder where my parents are," I said to Viola, after the plane took off.

"They probably got on at the last minute. You should go and find them. I bet they're in First Class."

I got up and walked to the front of the plane. Sure enough, there they were, with my sister. I felt nervous.

"I see you're flying to Atlanta."

"Yes, we're on our way to a wedding in South Carolina and a week of golfing," my father said. "Did you see this?" He handed me a newspaper. The headline read, "Emory Psychiatry Professor Found to Have Undisclosed Income from Pharmaceutical Company." I scanned it quickly. It appeared that Nemeroff had received over two million dollars in payments over the past several years from GSK, which represented a conflict of interest with a grant from the NIH to study GSK's antidepressant drug. My father knew that Nemeroff was the chair of my department and that we worked together.

"No, I didn't. This looks bad." What was going on here?

"What do you think will happen?"

"He'll probably have to resign." He was always telling me that I was going to get in trouble for speaking out about the pharmaceutical industry. And look at what happened. It was sudden; I was shocked.

"Why don't you give me a call on your way back to the airport in Atlanta? Maybe we could have dinner or something."

"Whatever works," my stepmother said. She didn't look happy with me. I got the feeling that I wouldn't hear from them.

"How'd it go?" Viola asked me when I got back to my seat.

"A little awkward. Could have been worse. At least I got it over with. I told them to give me a call when they came back through Atlanta. We'll see how that pans out."

# CHAPTER 58

A few weeks after the ceremony, I got an email from the husband of Jeanne Turnbow.

"I saw the Web site you made for the ceremony that you had for your mother," he wrote. "It was very moving. I had the strongest feeling that she was there watching the entire event. She was unbelievably happy, and there was nothing but pure unconditional love around her. It made me cry. There was also a strong feeling of liberation, as if a burden had been finally lifted."

I didn't know how to respond to this. I felt tears welling up in my eyes.

"I remember your mother driving her bright Paul Volkswagen convertible down Fishtrap Road with her scarf flying behind her. She reminded me of Isadore Duncan."

I didn't know what he meant, so I googled her name. She was an American who was a famous dancer in the 1940s, and was famous for being a free spirit and a Bohemian. She moved to France where she spent the remainder of her life. One time she was seen getting into the convertible sports car of an Italian man, to ride off with him for a tryst. She was quoted as saying "To life!" as she drove off, but her friends said that she actually said "To love!" In any case, her flowing scarf got caught in the spokes of the wheel of the car, and she was pulled to her death.

He commented on the fact that I grew up and became a psychiatrist, just like my father. In the years when I was growing up, he ran a New Age bookstore in Olympia. He talked about his ideas related to alternative medicine. He said that I should round out my medical education. I had to agree that the medical system in this country was distorted. People in the healthcare system say they want to help people, but the for-profit healthcare system drove doctors and hospital administrators to try to make money. A for-profit healthcare system was unethical.

People tried to accumulate as many pebbles as they can, thinking that will make them secure, and safeguard their families. But they could never accumulate enough pebbles. In the end, it led to ruin. We were not put in this place to accumulate pebbles. And the role of doctors is certainly not to accumulate pebbles. The role of doctors is to make people well, in spirit and in body.

He sent me a book about a man with a medical education who went into trances and "diagnosed" sick people and prescribed treatments.

I looked at the book. There are many rivers, and they all lead to one place. There are many spirits, and they all live in this world and a thousand others, this life and many more, whirling around like the rain kicked up by the Thunderbird. And they carry themselves from one life to the next, like a photographic imprint. Souls start from one source, are blasted through the universe to live in a gazillion bodies, and then come back to the primary source. They try to use the knowledge gained in previous lives to make the current one better. Or they try to undo the traumas and the tragedies of past lives in the current life. We labor away with our backs to the giant scoreboard of Karma. We cannot turn around, but it is always behind us. Ultimately, no matter what life, planet, universe, or time frame we are in, we all end up back in the same place, the source of all souls.

The river is always moving, but it always stays the same, said Heraclitus. When I was 20 years old, working in the salmon canneries in Alaska, we walked out into the wilderness and drank some tea laced with hallucinogenic mushrooms, and sat by the edge of a fast-flowing river, fed by glaciers.

"Look at the river, Doug!" one of my friends shouted at me.

Look at the river, Doug. Look at the riverDoug. Look at the riverDoug. Was I looking at the river, or was I looking at a fusion of myself and the river? I started to fall toward the river. We would become one. The current was moving strong, which meant certain death. At the last minute, my friend grabbed the back of my shirt, and pulled me back.

"Ha ha ha! You were almost a gonner, man!"

# CHAPTER 59

My mother's friend told me that if someone died suddenly, part of their energy, called the astral shell, was left in the place they died. He felt that my mother's astral shell had been left in our old house on Puget Sound.

I found myself thinking more and more about the old house. It was built in the Japanese style, surrounded by a covered porch, with rice mats on the floors and screens made out of rice paper. There was a garden in the front with a Japanese-style foot bridge and bamboo. In the last picture taken of my siblings and me before our mother died, we were standing on that bridge.

I wondered about my mother. I had found the location of her physical remains, but was there something else? Could she have more in store for me? Was there something else that I had to find in my quest? I couldn't stop thinking about her. Maybe her astral shell really was still in the house. I had to find out who was living there.

I found the name of the owner of the old house online. I gave her a call. It turned out she was a psychiatrist, just like me.

"I was just meeting with my interior designer last week," she said. "I heard that a woman died here many years ago. I asked if I should be concerned about the spirits of people who once lived here if I made a major transformation of the house."

"I'm sure that my mother wouldn't want to stop the house from being fixed. But I know she loved the house, and the Japanese theme fit in with her spiritual beliefs. I would really like to see the house, since I haven't been back there since my mother died, and it sounds like it is essentially unchanged. Maybe if I came out, you would feel more comfortable going ahead with the renovations."

I had plans to attend a scientific conference out of town, and I arranged to make a screwy detour through the Seattle airport so I could get down to see the house.

As I drove my rental car toward the house I came to the fork in the road with the lovely pasture with rolling hills surrounded by tall evergreens. I turned to the right, and moved on through the towers of trees on either side of the road, then made a turn into the driveway. Sheep looked at me, silently. I turned the key in the ignition and walked toward the house. I was in a flood of memories. The woman met me at the door.

"Welcome," she said. Some of her friends were at the house. I realized that they were curious about the former inhabitant. I felt shy. I walked around the house.

There was my parents' room, where I had seen pieces of dust illuminated by the early morning sun when I walked into their room in the early morning. I thought they were atoms. Here was the master bathroom, where my sister had seen our mother lying on the floor, vomiting, before she was taken away from us forever. This was the room where our nanny kept me confined while she drank Cokes and watched television, after my mother died. She had flirted with

my father. I remembered it even as a child of five. Too
bad her marriage fantasies didn't pan out. There were
the steep steps leading up to the loft bedroom where
my brother and I stayed. I had fallen down those stairs.
The memory came back to me for the first time in 40
years. Thonk! That hurt. The Zenmaster hits the
disciple on the head with a stick. Thonk!

I went out and sat on the Japanese porch and
watched the rain falling on the bamboos and
rhododendrons. Even though the house had decayed
over 40 years, it still had its Japanese design, and you
could detect the remains of a Japanese garden in front.
There was a feeling of karmic peace there. I thought
about my mother's love of Buddhist koans, like what is
the sound of one hand clapping? What was your face
before you were born? Riddles, really, meant to quicken
the mind.

I headed for the front door of the house.

"You're always welcome to see the house at any
time."

"What's the story with the sheep?"

"The prior owner was a physician. He was a friend
of the family, and moved to a community for the
elderly. I got the house through the family and didn't
know what to do with the sheep. So I became a
shepherdess. Here is some yarn I spun from their wool.
Why don't you take it home?"

"My wife likes knitting. Maybe she can make
something from it. My mother was a Buddhist, and
they believe in reincarnation. I have often thought that
she would like to have been reincarnated as one of the
sheep living on this property. She always loved it here."

"I certainly love it here. It's my refuge."

"I think my mother approves of your renovation plans. And I appreciate you letting me see the house again."

After I got into the car, the rain increased to a steady drumbeat against the windshield. I felt like I was getting somewhere now. Finally. I didn't have the answers to all of my questions. I wasn't sure I ever would. But I sure as hell knew a lot more now than I did a couple of years ago. Both about myself, and my mother. The two things were, of course, related.

I thought about the time when I was in college, and I used to visit my brother and sister and their young kids. I would always pick up the babies and put them in each of the four corners of the room. I wanted to give them a different perspective, looking at things from above, and from multiple points of view. The act of looking can change reality. It's one of the laws of physics. They call it quantum mechanics.

Viola and I had started marital counseling based on the recommendation of my psychiatrist. Things were getting better. It would take time, but it was worth it. I had gone for 40 years not showing emotion and crying only once or twice. Now I felt like a well of emotion, and I cried all the time. I thought about what my mother would think about me now. I thought she would be proud.

I had come back for her, and I found myself.

As I drove away through the rain-soaked road that ran like a corridor through towering fir trees, the astral shell escaped into the night sky.

# CHAPTER 60

Our marital therapist suggested that Viola and I start taking classes together, so that we could develop some mutual interests. We flipped coins to decide who would get to pick the first class. I won. I picked sailing. Her pick was painting. We would do that next.

After we finished the sailing class, we took Lucca and Lucia with us for a day of sailing. As we drove to the lake, I saw the familiar swaying of the trees in the wind that told me my mother was with us again. I didn't tell Viola. I didn't want to aggravate her.

We walked down to the beach. I remembered my childhood on Puget Sound, watching the crabs on the beach. When you approached, they would scamper backwards into their little holes that lined the farthest reach of the ocean surf. When I was in medical school, we spent many hours in our cubicles, studying. One of our favorite late night study break games was to pretend we were crabs, coming in and out of our cubicles. When you walked forward through life, things didn't always go according to plan.

We unrolled the jib sheet and tied it to a line with a Bowden knot. I went down into the berth to check the life jackets. The waves sloshed the boat around. I remembered being down in the berth of the cabin cruiser we had at the old Fishtrap house on Puget Sound when my mother was still alive. I remembered being down there with her while my father was above, steering the boat. I realized that was the only memory I had of her.

I remembered something from the transcript of her ceremony where a friend recalled seeing her with her family on our boat. She looked like she was happy then, he said.

I started the motor and steered the boat out of the dock. When we got out away from the marina, I told Viola to hoist the mainsail. Lucca and Lucia stayed below decks, listening to their iPods. Viola and I worked the sails together. We were working better now than before.

"Ready to tack!" I called out.

# CHAPTER 61

Viola and I signed up for an art class in an institute housed in one of the old mansions once owned by the Coca-Cola family. The art teacher played music on a CD player while we painted. Our assignment that night was to paint a still life from some objects on a table in the center of the room. I developed it into a scene that incorporated the dream I had of my mother when I was seven years old. I painted the outline of the trees against the night sky that had both been in the dream as well as in the park across the street from my house in Atlanta, where I had remembered my earliest reactions to my mother leaving me. One of the objects was a little figure that looked like a snake with a human face. I made him into me. My mother became a book with a dove on the cover. She always did like to read. There was a ray of light connecting me to her.

The art teacher stopped by my canvas. "Interesting."

"It's like the paintings of the Holy Ghost." I didn't know what I was talking about.

Just then, the CD player played a song from Coldplay.

*Bones are sinking like stones*
*All that we fall for*
*Homes places we've grown*
*All of us are done for*

*And we live in a beautiful world (yeah we do yeah
we do)*
   *We live in a beautiful world*

I recognized it as the song I had heard a few years
before, when I was sitting on the couch talking to my
daughter and reading the documents related to the
Roche and Accutane trials. I was having trouble
painting because my eyes were full of tears. I was glad
to be there with my wife, Viola. I was glad that she had
stayed and not given up on me. Was this more than a
coincidence? I thought about Jung and synchronicity. I
thought about how my father had handed me the
newspaper about Nemeroff's undisclosed income from
the drug company on the very day when we had our
ceremony for our mother. Was that another example of
synchronicity? Or was that something Oedipal? Were
the spirits telling me that this was the end of my story?
What did the Thunderbird say? Or could he even
speak?

I didn't know what was going on with the Roche
cases, whether I would be dragged up in front of
another judge and humiliated. Smith and Ryan weren't
keeping me in the loop.

I tried to push that out of my mind. *Just stay in
the moment*, I thought; *Enjoy it. Relax.*

I looked over to see what Viola was painting. Then
I went back to my canvas.

# CHAPTER 62

"Lucca's sick. I'm worried about him." Viola walked into the library, where I was working on my laptop.

"What's wrong?"

"He's got fever and joint pain."

"He had that a couple of weeks ago. I wonder if he has spondylitis like my mother?" Spondylitis is an autoimmune disease that runs in families. In affected patients, the body wrongly decides that its own cartilage and joints are foreign bodies, and so it tells the immune system, which normally protects against disease caused by bacteria and other foreign organisms, to attack itself.

I knew that my mother had a crippling limp, because I remembered her limping when she carried me around when I was a child. I never did get a clear medical history about my mother from my father. I was always afraid to bring up the topic. I made the diagnosis on my own when I was in medical school, just by reading rheumatology textbooks. I didn't really feel like talking to my father then, but I thought that maybe if I appealed to my need for medical information that was relevant to my son, that he might talk to me about it.

"I think you should call your father and ask about your mother's health history," Viola said. "It's important."

I picked up the phone. I was nervous.

"Lucca's been having some fever and joint pains," I told my father. "I remember that Laurnell used to walk with a limp. Can you tell me more about her medical history?"

"She did have a limp. She was diagnosed with spondylitis." I'd never heard him say that before. When I went out there for the funeral, I mentioned the fact that her obituary said that she had polio, and he had merely snapped, "She didn't have polio!" without any further elaboration, and I had left it there.

"Can you tell me about what happened when she died?" I was starting to sweat.

"She had bacterial meningitis."

"How do you know it was bacterial?"

"I was there when the doctor performed the tap." He was referring to the lumbar puncture, where a needle is inserted into the spaces between the vertebral bodies of the spine, to obtain cerebrospinal fluid from the sac that surrounds the spinal cord. "Her cerebral spinal fluid was full of pus." That meant that she had a raging bacterial infection. There was nothing more to say.

"OK, thanks." I hung up the phone. I walked downstairs to the living room where Viola was. "Well, that wasn't very pleasant. But at least I found out for sure how my mother died."

"How do you know?"

"My father said that her cerebrospinal fluid had pus in it. He was there and saw it when they tapped her. I don't think he would make that up."

The steroids she probably was on for the treatment of spondylitis would have impaired her immune system and made her more susceptible to infections, but as a four-year-old, I wasn't available for a consultation on her medication list. And they probably weren't as aware of the dangers of steroids back then as they are now."

## CHAPTER 63

I was back in Dr. S.'s office.

"How did the ceremony go?" she asked.

"It went fine. I'm glad that she at last got the recognition that she deserves, rather than just tossed into a pit and forgotten about."

"I'm sure she appreciates what you did for her."

"I talked to my father about my mother's death. I had an excuse because Lucca was having some joint pain or something. I mean he can't deny me medical information that can be necessary for Lucca, if he has a familial medical disorder, can he?"

"What'd he say?"

"Well, it was clear from the way he described it that she died from bacterial meningitis."

"Why?

"He said that the cerebrospinal fluid was dark yellow in color. Like it was full of puss. There probably wasn't anything anyone could have done about it."

"Well, at least you don't have to worry about the possibility that he could have somehow been responsible for her death. How does that make you feel?"

"Relieved."

"How are things going with the Accutane cases?"

"I'm getting deposed by Roche again tomorrow." Just thinking about it made my stomach turn.

"I'm sorry to hear about that. Do you really need to keep doing that work?"

"When I started, I was excited about the money. But I don't care about that anymore."

"So why are you doing it?"

"I couldn't look those family members who lost a child to suicide in the eye if I pulled out now. Besides those plaintiffs' lawyers would probably kill me."

"I'll bet."

"I couldn't believe it when the Bishop family from Florida dropped their case. I went through so much suffering. And for what? That case had the best chance of winning."

"That must have been a disappointment for you."

"Somehow I equate these cases with the struggle I went through over my mom. I wonder if the two events are somehow cosmically connected."

"You wouldn't have the strength and sense of determination you needed to keep on with that battle if you didn't have the resources of your mother to help you out. She seems like she was quite a woman."

"I wish she could be here to see this happen. She was always an advocate kind of person."

"I'm sure she would be proud of you."

There was nothing else to say. We were out of time. The dread of the upcoming deposition filled my brain like dirty water flowing where there is nothing to stop it.

# CHAPTER 64

That night I had dinner with the attorney representing the plaintiff in this particular case. I had never met her before. Her name was Julie. She was from Texas. The attorneys and cases were all running together in my mind.

"You're different than I had imagined you," she said.

"Why, what were you expecting?"

"After reading all that stuff that Roche wrote about you in their legal briefs, I would have expected some sleazy psychiatrist out to make some money by working as an expert witness."

"Yeah, well. What do expect from them? The money hasn't been worth it, actually. Believe it or not, I am mostly motivated by the principle of the thing. I just hope some of these people get a day in court."

"Roche's Accutane Sales have been tanking lately. Doctors don't want to prescribe it if they have to sign up for a registry. Your writings and research have gone a long way to warning people about the potential dangers."

"I'm glad something good is coming out of this. It seems like every week I am hearing about another Accutane psych horror story."

We spent the rest of dinner going over the case. That night I forced myself to re-read old depositions and my reports. I couldn't stand it. I had been deposed so many times, I was afraid that this was going to be number 13. Being a little superstitious, I was afraid to count.

The next morning, getting dressed, I passed over the pinstripe suit I usually wore and went for a light beige. They said that people respect you more when you wear something dark, but I knew it was just going to be me and Colleen Hennessey and the attorney for the plaintiff's family. Colleen didn't have any respect for me anyway, so what did I care?

As I drove to the legal offices downtown where the deposition was scheduled to take place, I went over the previous depositions. "Deposition X" I called it in my mind, so as to avoid worrying about whether it was the unlucky number 13.

Colleen was there in her usual beige pants suit when I walked into the room. "I can tell how much alcohol someone drinks just by looking at them," she said to one of the attorneys that worked for Roche.

I thought about knocking back some beers with Colleen. Didn't seem like it would be much fun. Her comment reminded me of my stepmother saying that she judged people by what kind of shoes they wore and what condition they were in. I looked down at my shoes. Light brown leather, in good condition, matched my suit. OK so far.

The court reporter wired me up with a mic and we got into action.

"Doctor, can alcohol cause depression?" Colleen jabbed at her yellow legal pad with her pen.

"That depends." I knew where this was going.

"On what, doctor?"

"On how much one drank, what stage of withdrawal you were in." What would my mother do? She certainly wouldn't cave in to this corporate poodle, just because she criticized her.

"Wouldn't you agree, Doctor, that drinking can make you suicidal."

"That depends on the situation."

"If someone were drinking and his doctor prescribed Accutane, and the patient killed himself, wouldn't you conclude that the alcohol is what made him do it?"

"Alcohol could have contributed, but so could the Accutane. You can't exclude the possibility that Accutane caused someone to kill himself, just because he drank alcohol."

I locked eyes with Colleen for just a moment. I tried to figure out if she was giving me a look of hatred or contempt. Then I let it go. What did I care, anyway? She dropped that bone and flipped through her notes.

After another couple of hours of gritting it out, we broke for lunch. Julie and I headed for a barbecue place across the street. It was a sunny and pleasant day, and we sat out on the back porch of the restaurant.

"You were really good in there," Julie said.

"Practice makes perfect. I lost track of how many times I've been deposed, but it is about 15 I think."

"Something's working."

"Things seem different from the old days. It's like they're slacking off or something."

"You've done a lot of damage to their market share. I wouldn't underestimate it."

"Well, if one life was saved, it's worth it." I thought about my mother. I wondered what she would think about this. I didn't have to spend much time on it before I had my answer. I thought about how I talked to Dr. S. about what it meant to me to write a book about prescription medications that went against the huge marketing machine of the pharmaceutical industry. About how I had written it for my mother. And truth. The night after that session, I had cried for hours.

"I get the feeling that Roche may be giving up on this drug," Julie said. "They have a lot of liability hanging over their heads. I think they want to wrap things up and move on to their next blockbuster drug."

"Yeah, like Tamiflu. I call it bird flu drugs for bird brains. If the bird flu mutates so that it can be transmitted to humans, the drug won't work anymore, anyway. But that doesn't stop them from using people like Dick Cheney to push it so they can make their billions."

After lunch, we walked back to the legal offices, and I got hooked up with the mic again.

"I'd like to enter this into the record as Exhibit #15." Colleen pushed a piece of paper across the table.

"Could you identify this for the record, please?" She had a smug look on her face, like an I-got-you-this-time kind of look.

"It's a copy of one of my blogs I wrote." I had been writing a blog about medical topics in the news to promote my latest book on prescription medications. I wasn't surprised that she had found that on the Internet.

"Could you read the sentence I have outlined there?"

"Statistics can be used in whatever way you want."

"Do you agree with that statement?"

"Not really."

"Why did you write it then?"

"It's a blog. Sometimes I say sarcastic things there. Blogs are not meant to be taken seriously. Have you been enjoying my blog, Colleen?"

"How did you know we were reading it?" She was shocked.

"I have a program that allows me to see who has been reading my Web sites. I can see when and where, and what they are reading and for how long. You must have really enjoyed reading it. You've been reading it every day for the past six months."

"Well, I don't know what to say—"

"—did you read it yourself?"

"Actually, we had an intern read it." She shuffled through some more of my blog posts. Apparently she decided that she wasn't going to get any blood out of this one because she moved on.

I drove home with the top of the car down. My brain was fried like usual after these depositions, but somehow I felt less out of control than usual. That night, I sat in the library with and counted the number of transcripts I had from previous depositions.

This one was number 15. I couldn't remember which one was 13, and I didn't want to.

Maybe my luck was getting better.

## CHAPTER 65

One day, a few months later, I came to work and found a message on my voice mail. The first was from Kris West. I called her back right away.

"I just wanted to let you know that the committee investigating the charges of fraud against you from Roche has issued its final report. They said they found no evidence of fraud. They'll be forwarding their report to the journal that published your paper."

"That's great news! Thanks for letting me know." I didn't know whether to trust my ears. "So what happens next?"

"Nothing. We'll inform the journal of our findings. That's it. It's over."

"What about the NIH Office of Research Compliance thing?"

"We gave them our report a year ago. We didn't hear from them again, and closed the case. All of your inquiries are over. That's it."

I hung up the phone. I felt like I had a near miss with a freight train. I still didn't trust my feelings. Was it really over?

\* \* \*

It wasn't long after that that I got a call from Mike Ryan. It was June of 2009.

"Doctor Bremner, did you hear the news? Roche just announced that they are taking Accutane off of the market."

"Really?" I was amazed. "Why is that?"

"They said it was a business decision."

"What the hell does that mean?"

"It means that their Sales were dragging because of all the negative publicity and the lawsuits were starting to pile up against them."

"Wow, that's amazing! It went from being a billion-dollar-a-year drug to being removed from the market in just a few years!" I said.

"Your research and speaking out went a long way to raising awareness about the risks of this drug."

"I just wish that families like the Bishops got some justice along the way. Thanks for letting me know."

I walked outside. The day was failing, and I moved into the womb-like heat of the Georgia night. The fireflies swooned and fell in luminous arcs. Crepe myrtle and banana trees winked, and a chorus of cicadas lobbed into the night as they had done since the beginning of time.

# CHAPTER 66

I was sitting on the couch, watching a movie with Viola. Things were going better with us these days. I knew it would take her a long time for her to trust me again after all of my shenanigans, but she seemed willing to give it a try. She was knitting me a scarf from the wool I had gotten from the sheep given to me by the psychiatrist-shepherdess. She had been working on it for weeks. I jokingly called her Penelope, after the wife of Ulysses, who had promised to marry the suitors when she finished what she was sewing, but who undid everything she had done during the day at night, so as to delay giving herself away.

My daughter was applying to college now. I took advantage of her college search to spend time with her driving through New England, Ohio, and Pennsylvania, looking at colleges. We had some good times, along with the usual arguments.

And then, one day, Viola finished her scarf. It had the original, undyed wool of the three sheep from our family's farm. I wrapped it around my neck. I felt as if my mother were back with me again.

It was an act of love.

CPSIA information can be obtained
at www.ICGtesting.com
Printed in the USA
LVHW011340170521
687652LV00035B/2380